M000035643

# FIRST LATIN

## A Language Discovery Program

### BOOK I
*Language and Family*

### BOOK II
*Daily Life*

### Marion Polsky

Longman

**in memory of Ruthie**

**First Latin, A Language Discovery Program, Student Activity Books I & II**

Copyright © 1990 by Longman
All rights reserved.
No part of this publication may be reproduced,
stored in a retrieval system, or transmitted
in any form or by any means, electronic, mechanical,
photocopying, recording, or otherwise,
without the prior permission of the publisher.

Longman, 95 Church Street, White Plains, N.Y. 10601


Associated companies:
Longman Group Ltd., London
Longman Cheshire Pty., Melbourne
Longman Paul Pty., Auckland
Copp Clark Pitman, Toronto

*Some of the art in the Cue Cards is based on art originally appearing in First Latin: The
Discovery of Language, by Marion Polsky.*

Executive editor: Lyn McLean
Production editor: Helen B. Ambrosio
Text design: Caliber Design Planning, Inc.
Cover illustration/photo: Caliber Design Planning, Inc.
Text art: Caliber Design Planning, Inc. and Eulala Conner, Publisher's Graphics Inc.
Production supervisor: Kathleen M. Ryan

Consultants: John J. Langton, Professor Gilbert Lawall, Dr. Rudolph Masciantonio

Audio cassette performers: Marion Polsky, John J. Langton, Christine Ranck, Jay Berliner
Audio cassette producer: The Sun Group


ISBN: 0-8013-0570-5


ABCDEFGHIJ - MU - 99 98 97 96 95 94 93 92 91 90

# Student Activity Book I

# Contents

# Part ONE

# *The Roman Experience*

In this unit, you will:

learn to greet people in Latin, with your Latin name
identify places in the world in Latin
sing songs in Latin
read about Roman gods and heroes
solve Latin arithmetic problems
find out about city life in ancient Rome
act in Roman skits
discover the connection between Latin and English words

# LECTIŌ I

# Rōmānī Antīquī

## The Romans Tell Their Story

The Latin language, which you have been practicing, was originally spoken thousands of years ago by a people called the **Romans**. These ancient Romans built a great and powerful civilization.

Here are some famous figures from the Roman past, telling the story of Rome's beginnings and rise to power. Every Roman boy and girl knew by heart these tales of bravery, honor, and loyalty to Rome. Find the *name* of each speaker under his picture and copy it in the blank at the end of the speech.

**Aeneas**

"Over three thousand years ago, there was a great war between the **Greeks** and my people, the **Trojans**, who lived across the sea. I escaped with a small band of men, carrying my father on my back and clutching the hand of my small son. I traveled for 10 years, protected by my mother, the beautiful goddess **Venus**. I finally settled in **Italy**, in an area called Latium. There a people called the Latins were living. Their king, **Latinus**, gave me his daughter in marriage. The Trojans and the Latins soon became one nation, and I was the ruler. We all spoke **Latin**, the language of the Latin people."

**Romulus and Remus**

"My brother **Remus** and I were twins, sons of Rhea Silvia and the god of war, **Mars**. We came from the long bloodline of our great ancestor Aeneas. Our wicked uncle ordered us to be thrown into the Tiber River to drown, but we floated safely to a river bank, where we were found and nursed by a she-wolf. Much later we returned to **Alba Longa**, our birthplace, killed our evil uncle, and put our grandfather **Numitor** back on the throne.

"Remus and I left to build a *new city*. We argued because we both wanted to be king, but the gods sent me a special sign—twelve birds circling my head. On **April**

**21, 753 B.C.**, I built the walls of the city and named it **Roma**, after myself. When my brother mocked the walls, I killed him. No one would ever again scorn Rome, the great city of _____."

**Horatius**

"Many years after Rome was built, the people drove out the last king, **Tarquin the Proud**. They wanted to be free, so in **509 B.C.** they set up a new form of government, a **republic**, with a constitution and elected officials. But a foreign king tried to put Tarquin back in power at Rome. While Rome was preparing for battle, I alone held off the king and all his forces at the head of a bridge. When the bridge was destroyed, I refused to surrender. Badly wounded, I leaped into the Tiber River and swam back to Rome in full armor." _____ .

"I swore to kill the same foreign king and sneaked into his camp. I was caught. To show how courageous we Romans are, I put my right hand on hot coals and burned it away. The king was impressed and decided to make peace with the Romans. I got the nickname **Scaevola**, 'Lefty.' " _____ .

**Mucius Scaevola**

**Julius Caesar**

"I was a great general, and probably the most famous Roman in history. I conquered many nations for Rome. I became so powerful that many citizens feared I would put an end to the Roman Republic. I was murdered on **March 15, 44 B.C.**, stabbed to death by my best friend, Brutus, and others in the Senate House."

_____ .

"I, **Octavian**, was adopted by my great-uncle Julius Caesar and inherited his fortune after he was murdered. I had control of most of Rome and was able to bring about a long peace following many years of bloodshed between Romans. In **27 B.C.** I received the supreme title _____, which means "the honored one," and I am known in history by this name. The eighth month in the calendar is named for me. As the first emperor, I made Rome the greatest power in the Western world. The **Roman Empire** lasted 500 years."

**Augustus**

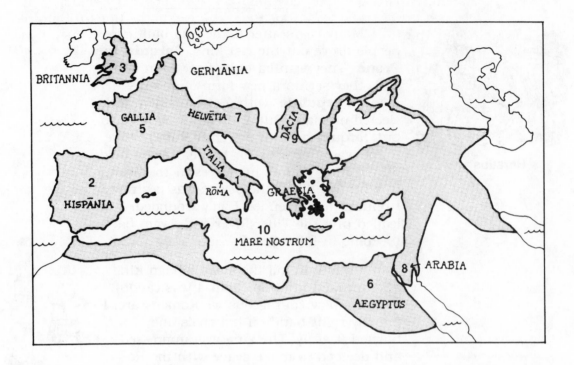

This is a map of the Roman Empire. The places have their Latin names.

    1. Locate each place listed below and put its number on the map.

    2. Next to each place on the list, put the modern English name.

You will see that many countries once were part of the Roman Empire. Today, Rome is still the largest city in Italy, but the Roman Empire no longer exists.

| Ubi est . . . ? | Modern English Name |
|---|---|
| 1. Italia | Italy |
| 2. Hispānia | _____ |
| 3. Britannia | _____ |
| 4. Graecia | _____ |
| 5. Gallia | _____ |
| 6. Aegyptus | _____ |
| 7. Helvētia | Switzerland |
| 8. Arabia | _____ |
| 9. Dācia | Romania |
| 10. Mare Nostrum | Mediterranean Sea |

**Latin** is the mother of the **Romance** languages—Spanish, French, Italian, Portuguese, and Rumanian. These daughter languages developed in the parts of Europe that belonged to the Roman Empire. When the Romans conquered new lands, they brought their language, Latin, with them. Latin was the common language for all peoples living in the great Roman Empire.

Put the names of the Romance languages in the tree. Latin is the root.

LATIN

You can see for yourself that the Romance languages are related to Latin:

| **Latin** | Italian | French | Spanish | Portuguese | Rumanian |
|-----------|---------|--------|---------|------------|----------|
| **ūnus** | uno | un | uno | um | un |
| **dūo** | due | deux | dos | dois | doi |
| **trēs** | tre | trois | tres | trez | trei |

How does **English** fit in?

English is not a Romance language. Its origins are in another mother language, **Germanic**, which is also the mother of modern German.

BUT—Latin vocabulary (words) entered the English language from its very beginning, and the process is still going on! *Computer, camera, video* all come from Latin. So, about three out of every five English words have Latin roots. Put ENGLISH in the section of the two trees that overlap:

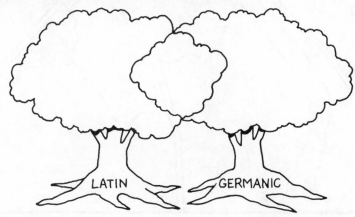

LATIN          GERMANIC

# Rōma Est Magna!

## A Tour of the City

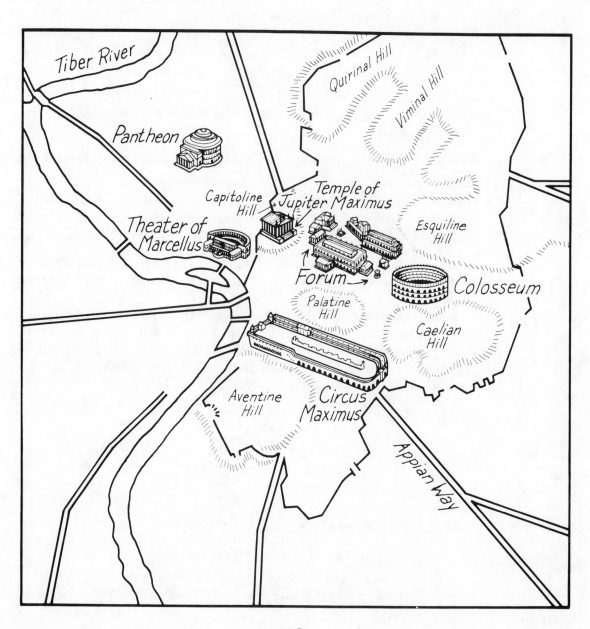

If you lived in the city of Rome about 110 A.D., you might meet Lucius, who is 11 years old. His cousin Cornelia is visiting from Abellinum, a small town in southern Italy. The two are discussing the sights and planning a tour. This is Cornelia's first trip to the big city.

As you read, think about buildings and places in your own home town which may be like the ones Lucius describes here.

Locate on the city map each building you see printed in *italics*.

CORNELIA: "I can't believe I'm finally here! I want to see everything—the Colosseum, the Circus Maximus, the Temple of Jupiter, the Pantheon, the Palace of Augustus, the Theater of Marcellus, and the Baths of our wonderful Emperor Trajan. And I want to do lots of shopping in the Forum. How about a picnic on the banks of the Tiber River, too?"

LUCIUS: "Hold on, hold on! Nobody can visit all those places in one day. **Rōma est magna!** You saw that for yourself when you arrived. By the way, how did you get here?"

CORNELIA: "I came in a carriage with some other travelers from the South. We took the Appian Way, of course. I saw the tombs all along the roadside; many had lifelike statues of the dead. They were pretty scary. I admit I was impressed by the huge aqueduct leading into the city. We Romans are great engineers!"

LUCIUS: "I can see you are excited. I'm proud of my city. It's the center of the whole Empire. As the saying goes, 'All roads lead to Rome'! I'll tell you about some of the sights you mentioned, and then you can decide what to do, okay?

"The *Colosseum* is the first thing to see. It's the round building in the center of the city, and it's gigantic—187 feet high and 1,729 feet around! You can watch gladiator contests there, and fights between men and animals. My father won't let me go to these. If we're lucky, while you're here, they'll flood the whole floor of the amphitheater with water from underground pipes, so you can see a naval battle or ship race—my favorite.

"After that, go to the *Circus Maximus*, the very first Roman race course, and the biggest of the three in the city. There are terrific chariot races—you can place a bet, if you like. Sometimes it gets so crowded that people pass out from the heat, but we usually go early to get good seats. I hear it's being enlarged and someday will hold 250,000 people.

"Sometimes my parents take me to the *Theater of Marcellus*. I like the comedies best, especially when someone gets hit over the head. But sometimes it's so noisy I can't hear what the actors are saying. That's why the pantomimes are good. They have dancing, singing, and a live orchestra, and you can figure out what's going on just by watching.

"Tomorrow my big sister Claudia will take you to the *Forum* while I'm in school. There you can see the Black Stone, which marks the spot where Romulus is buried; the Curia, where my father and other senators meet; the enormous Temple of Saturn, father of our lord Jupiter; the Basilica Julia or law court, built by Julius Caesar; and many other famous buildings. You can also buy what you want. Claudia *loves* to go shopping.

"Keep in mind that Rome is built on seven hills, so you'll get tired walking. But we'll take you to the top of the Capitoline Hill, which overlooks the Forum, to visit the *Temple of Jupiter Maximus*, the most awesome in the whole city. I suppose Claudia will also show you the mansions on the Palatine Hill, because she likes to mix with the very rich. The Palace of Augustus is still there. I definitely think you should see the *Pantheon*, which has a huge dome. It's considered a wonder of the world, like the Pyramids of Egypt. And then there's—"

CORNELIA: "I can't listen anymore. Oh, Lucius, this is going to be the best vacation of my life! But I'm already exhausted. Now I understand why we say, 'Rome wasn't built in a day.'"

FĪNIS

## Time Traveler: Lucius Visits Your Town

Imagine that Lucius has arrived in your town by a magic time machine. What would you show him? How would you compare the sights to those in ancient Rome? What new types of buildings and public entertainment would surprise him? Write down your guided tour for Lucius on a separate piece of paper.

Roman men and boys had three names:

1. the **praenōmen**, similar to our first or given name.
2. the **nōmen**, similar to our last name. This was the clan name. All free-born Romans belonged to a clan, or large family group.
3. the **cognōmen**, which indicated a particular branch of the clan. We do not have this category of name in our system.

Here is an example:

| Marcus | Tullius | Cicerō |
|---|---|---|
| praenōmen | nōmen | cognōmen |

Daughter: Tullia
Son: Marcus Tullius Cicerō

You will notice that the daughter simply has the father's **nōmen**, with a feminine ending **-a**. What was Cornelia's father's **nōmen**? _____ If a family had more than one daughter, the girls were named by birth order: **Tullia Prīma** (first-born), **Tullia Secunda** (second-born), and so on. When the daughters got married, they added their husband's **nōmen** as their second name.

Sons often took their father's **praenōmen**, as in the example. More often, though, a boy's **praenōmen** stood for his birth order: **Prīmus, Secundus**, and so on. In fact, there were very few different first names in ancient Rome.

Here are some *actual* Roman names, either first names or clan names, that are still used in the United States (with English endings): Antony, Cecilia, Claudia, Cornelia, Emily, Julius, Julia, Lucy, Luke, Mark, Marcia.

Many other English names, however, come from real Latin *words*. Here are some: Alma, Amanda, Amy, Beatrice, Belle, Felix, Florence, Grace, Leo, Margaret, Max, Paul, Peter, Rose, Stella, Sylvia, Vera, Victor, Victoria, Vincent. You can find out the *meaning* of these names and the Latin words they come from by looking in an English dictionary.

What does *your* real first name mean? _____

What does your **praenōmen** in the class mean? _____

# In Urbe

## Duae Puellae

*It is 6:00 A.M. sunrise. Claudia, who is 13, awakens her cousin.*

CLAUDIA: "How did you sleep, Cornelia?"

CORNELIA: "To tell you the truth, not too well. There was a lot of noise outside—people shouting and singing until all hours, and wagon wheels clanking on the cobblestones all night."

CLAUDIA: "Oh, the people must have been guests coming home from our neighbor Trimalchio's big party. They probably drank too much wine! It's too bad we live near a major road. The work wagons use it to bring food and supplies to the city, but they're allowed to enter Rome only at night. I guess I'm used to the sound. Wake up, now! Let's go to the Forum."

*Claudia, Cornelia, and Lucius leave the house early, grabbing breakfast on the way—a sweet flat pancake at the baker's. In a building near the Forum, Cornelia hears some boys screaming and a man yelling at them.*

LUCIUS: "Uh-oh! Orbilius is in a bad mood, and I'm late."

CLAUDIA: "Better hurry up, **Lūcī**. Orbilius is the schoolteacher, Cornelia. He is very strict and sometimes hits his students. Good luck, **Lūcī**! **Valē**!"

*Lucius goes into the schoolroom. The two girls enter the Forum.*

CORNELIA: "I can't believe there are so many people in one place. Look at the dancers, Claudia! Why are they here? And what's that animal?"

CLAUDIA: "That's a baboon, a very rare pet! It belongs to the rich banker Fulvius. See him lying in that fancy litter, being carried by slaves all dressed up in silk and jewels? He likes to show off. Let's go see the acrobat. He's my favorite street entertainer."

CORNELIA: "Wait up, Claudia! I want to have my fortune told."

CLAUDIA: "No, Cornelia, be careful. Those fortune-tellers will try to cheat you. Look! There's a funeral procession right on the Via Sacra. The women are wailing and the trumpets are blasting. I can hardly hear. Let's hurry past them and get to the Rostra; maybe Aulus is giving a speech on the latest political scandal. Speakers at this spot like to yell out to the senators and other officials as they enter the Curia."

CORNELIA: "I noticed some soldiers across the way. People are cheering."

CLAUDIA: "Yes, they're back from a foreign war fought for our Emperor Trajan. They'll have a big victory parade tomorrow. Would you like to see the shops?"

*As the two girls walk along the shopping arcade, they see people of different nationalities and races selling wonderful goods from all over the world.*

CORNELIA: "Look at that fine blue silk. It would make a great **stola** for the banquet your father is giving in my honor."

CLAUDIA: "We'll see. I want to go to the goldsmith's shop for new earrings."

*Tired from shopping, the cousins decide to get a snack at the nearest food stand. They settle on smoked fish, cheese, bread, and some wine.*

CORNELIA: "Claudia, I'm exhausted. The crowds are enormous. I've never seen so many pushy people. The screaming is giving me a headache. Let's take our food and find a nice shady spot for a picnic. It's noon, and the sun is hot."

CLAUDIA: "Relax, Cornelia. Everybody's on edge by this hour. Soon all the shops and government houses will close down. Let's walk to the Baths. We'll eat our lunch on the way."

CORNELIA: "Perhaps we should walk north. Somebody told me the Subura district is nice."

CLAUDIA: "Oh, Cornelia, you have a lot to learn. The Subura is a very rough neighborhood, too dangerous to walk around in. And it's out of our way."

*On the way to the Baths, the girls find themselves on a narrow street.*

CLAUDIA: "Watch out, Cornelia! Here comes a carriage. Press yourself against this building, so it can pass."

CORNELIA: "I'm not used to such cramped spaces in my village. It's nice and quiet there and—Oh, no! Oh, no! Someone just spilled filthy cooking water on me from that apartment window. See it?"

CLAUDIA: "Oh, I'm sorry. I forgot to warn you about that. We should walk in the middle of the street. People sometimes do throw their garbage out the window. You have to watch where you step!"

*At the Baths, the two meet Claudia's friend, Livia. They have a wonderful time, washing, swimming, and gossiping.*

CLAUDIA: "We have to go home now. It's a long walk. Mother is expecting us for dinner. Besides, I don't have a torch to light our way once it gets dark."

CORNELIA: "Okay, Claudia. I hate to leave, though. These are the most beautiful baths I've ever seen; the marble and statues are really lovely."

CLAUDIA: "Yes, they are. Now I can't wait to take you to the theater and the races and other sights. How do you like Rome so far?"

CORNELIA: "Well, Claudia, it's exciting—full of things to do and interesting people and places. Everything's so big compared to where I live. Rome is a nice place to visit, but—I wouldn't want to live here."

CLAUDIA: "Little cousin, **dē gustibus nōn est disputandum**. But I bet you'll change your mind."

FĪNIS

## Then and Now: City Living

Find ten features of everyday life in ancient Rome that you might also find in a typical modern American city. Here's one to get you started: *crowds*.

# Fābella: Trēs Puellae

Persōnae: Claudia, Cornēlia, Līvia

CLAUDIA: Salvē, Līvia!

LĪVIA: Salvē, Claudia! *(turning to Cornelia)* Salvē! Quid est praenōmen tibi? Quis es?

CORNĒLIA: Salvē! Praenōmen mihi est Cornēlia. Consōbrīna Claudiae sum. Quid est praenōmen tibi?

LĪVIA: Praenōmen mihi est Līvia. Puella Rōmāna sum. Amīca Claudiae sum.

*Livia and Cornelia shake hands. The three girls walk to the Baths.*

***Vocabulary Help:***

consōbrīna Claudiae—Claudia's cousin

amīca Claudiae—Claudia's friend

In the picture above, find the Latin word for each of the following and write it in the blank:

| | | | |
|---|---|---|---|
| 1. teacher | *magistra* | 11. clock | _____ |
| 2. student (boy) | _____ | 12. picture | _____ |
| 3. student (girl) | _____ | 13. map | _____ |
| 4. desk/table | _____ | 14. board | _____ |
| 5. chair | _____ | 15. chalk | _____ |
| 6. door | _____ | 16. eraser | _____ |
| 7. window | _____ | 17. pen | _____ |
| 8. wall | _____ | 18. pencil | _____ |
| 9. room | _____ | 19. paper | _____ |
| 10. flag | _____ | 20. ruler | _____ |

**17**

# Mini-Review I

Praenōmen mihi est _____.
(Puer/Puella) _____ sum.
(Discipulus/Discipula) _____ sum.

## True or False?

Mark each statement below TRUE or FALSE.

1. _____ The Roman Forum was the center for business and government.

2. _____ Lucius watched acrobats and clowns in the Circus Maximus.

3. _____ In the Forum, Cornelia saw Fulvius, a banker, and his pet baboon.

4. _____ Ancient Rome was built on nine hills.

5. _____ The Subura was a wealthy district of the city.

6. _____ Romans went to the baths to relax and meet friends after work.

7. _____ The Pantheon was a temple with a huge dome.

8. _____ A Roman man's *first* name was his **nōmen**.

## Word Search: Roman Heroes

Find and circle the Latin names of the people and gods described below. Words may go across, down, or on the diagonal, but are never backward.

1. brother of Romulus
2. king of the Latins
3. founder of Rome
4. mother of Aeneas
5. "Lefty"
6. father of Romulus
7. first emperor of Rome
8. Julius __, a great general
9. hero at a bridge
10. Trojan who came to Italy

```
H O R A T I U S
A C M A R S I A
U A P R O R L E
G E N L S O A N
U S T R V M T E
S A D E E U I A
T R A M N L N S
U C U U U U U U
S S S S S S S S
```

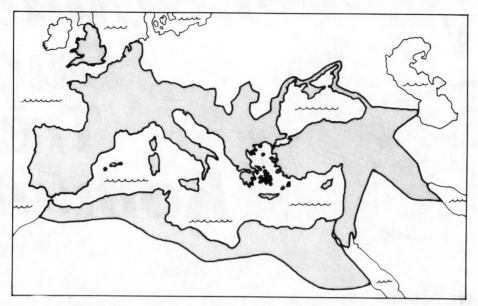

1. Find the modern English name for each place listed below and put it in the first column.

| England Spain Egypt Italy Romania France Germany Greece |
| --- |

| Latin Name | English Name | Language |
| --- | --- | --- |
| Italia | _____ | _____ |
| Britannia | _____ | _____ |
| Gallia | _____ | _____ |
| Hispānia | _____ | _____ |
| Aegyptus | _____ | _____ |
| Dācia | _____ | _____ |
| Graecia | _____ | _____ |
| Germānia | _____ | _____ |

2. In the second column above, place the name of the language now spoken in each country.

| German French Spanish Italian Rumanian Arabic Greek English |
| --- |

3. Put circles around the names of the four **Romance languages** in the column. Then complete this sentence: The mother of these languages is _____, which was the common language for all peoples living in the great _____ Empire.

# Ūnus, Duo, Trēs Rōmānī

## Numerī Rōmānī

In many civilizations, the fingers of the human hand are used for counting from 1 to 10. The Romans created their written numerals from this method of counting:

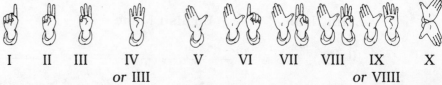

| I | II | III | IV | V | VI | VII | VIII | IX | X |

*or* IIII                                          *or* VIIII

ūnus  duo  trēs  quattuor  quīnque  sex  septem  octō  novem  decem

Count the objects in each row. Then put the Roman numeral in the first blank and the Latin word for the number in the second blank:

1. □□□□□     V     *quīnque*

2. ●●●△△△△△    _____    _____

3. ◆    _____    _____

4. ○○▼▼▼□    _____    _____

5. ◇◇◇◇    _____    _____

6. ▲▲▲▲▲▲▼    _____    _____

7. ◆◆◆△△△    _____    _____

8. ■■    _____    _____

9. △▽△▽△▽△    _____    _____

10. ●●●    _____    _____

By now you have seen that many English words can come from just one Latin word. Each Latin word has a root-form, and it is this form that is used to make English words. For example, **ūnus** (one) has the root-form **ūni-**.

In this book, each time a Latin word is presented for word study, the root-form of it will also be given to you. This form always ends in a hyphen to show you that it is not a word by itself, but it goes into making an English word.

Here are the root-forms for the numbers 1 to 4 in Latin:

(**ūnus**) **ūni-**   (**duo**) **du-**   (**trēs**) **tri-**   (**quattuor**) **quadr-**

You are now ready to build new words:

1. If a *quadrilateral* figure is a figure with *four* sides (from Latin **later-**, "side"), how many sides does a *trilateral* have? _____.

2. If a *triangle* has *three* angles, what is the word for a figure with *four* angles? _____.

3. If a *tricycle* is a vehicle with *three* wheels, what is the word for a vehicle with *one* wheel? _____.

As you know, a vehicle with two wheels is a *bicycle*. This word has a different Latin root that also means "two": **bi-** (Latin **bis**, "twice") + **cycle**. **Bi-** is used more often than **du-** to make English words.

4. If something that has two shapes in *biform*, what is the word for something that has *one* shape? _____

   *Three* shapes? _____.

5. **Pod-** and **ped-** are roots that mean "foot." How many feet does a *biped* have? _____ A *unipod*? _____ A *tripod*? _____

   A *quadruped*? _____.

6. The ending **-ple** (sometimes **-uple**) means "times." If you make something *four* times bigger, you *quadruple* it. If you make it *three* times bigger, you _____ it. But twice as big is *double*, not *biple*!

## I've Got Your Number

For each number set, choose the word from the list at the top that best completes each sentence.

**Ūnus, Ūni-**

UNILATERAL        UNITY        UNICORN        UNIFORM

1. A treaty that is one-sided is called a _____ agreement.

2. A mythological creature that has a horn on its head is a
_____.

3. Mary baked all the cookies the same size to make them
_____.

4. When Jim and Al agreed, they expressed a _____ of opinion.

**Trēs, Tri-**

TRIANGLE        TRIPLICATE        TRICOLOR        TRICEPS

1. A geometrical figure with three angles is a _____.

2. The three-headed muscle in the back of the upper arm is the
_____.

3. The French flag, which is blue, white, and red, is called the
_____.

4. Important reports are often made up in _____.

**Quattuor, Quadr-**

QUADRANGLE  QUADRUPED  QUADRUPLET  QUADRILATERAL

1. A human being is a biped, but a horse or a cow is a
_____.

2. A figure with four sides is a _____.

3. A figure having four angles is called a _____.

4. A baby who is one of four born at the same time is a
_____.

Sometimes you may *think* that a particular English word co
from a Latin root you recognize. But how do you know for sure? To
find out, you have to look in a good dictionary which contains
information on the history of the English word. This information is
enclosed in brackets like these: [     ]

Here's an example:

*unicorn*—a mythical creature usually represented as a horse with a
single horn. [Middle English, from Old French, from Latin **ūni-
cornis: ūni-**, "one" + **cornū**, "horn"]

Do you see the **ūni-** in the bracketed section?

Sometimes the names of the languages will be abbreviated:
ME—Middle English, OFr—Old French, L—Latin, LL—Late Latin,
and so on. All abbreviations are listed at the beginning of a dictionary, so you can check the full name of the language. Look for **Latin**,
**L**, **LL**, or **Lat** to prove that the English word comes from Latin.

## Sample Problem

The Latin word **spīna** (thorn, spine) has the root-form **spīn-**. How
many of the following unusual English words come from the Latin?
*spinel*, *spinach*, *spinet*. Look at the dictionary entries below to find
out. Circle any English word that has a Latin connection.

*spinach*—a cultivated plant with edible leaves [< OFr **espinache** <
OSp **espinaca** < Arab *isfānākh*]

*spinel*—any of several hard-colored minerals with sharply pointed
crystals [< F **spinelle** < It **spinella** = **spīn**(a), thorn < L + **ella**
diminutive suffix < L]

*spinet*—a small upright piano [variation of **espinette** < F < It
**spinetta**, possibly named after Giovanni **Spinetti**, its inven-
tor, about 1503]

Language abbreviations: F—French, It—Italian, L—Latin, OFr—Old
French, OSp—Old Spanish, Arab—Arabic

Are there *other* English words from Latin **spīn-**? You bet! Open
the dictionary!

# LECTIŌ V

# Rōmānus, Rōmāna

## Quis Est . . . ? (Who Is . . . ?)

Lūcius et Claudia sunt duo Rōmānī.

Quis est Lūcius? Quis est Claudia?

Write out sentences as answers to the following questions in the space provided. Start your sentence with either **Lūcius** or **Claudia**:

Quis est Rōmāna? _____ *Claudia est Rōmāna.* _____

Quis est Rōmānus? _____

Quis est discipulus? _____

Quis est puella? _____

Quis est discipula? _____

Quis est puer? _____

## Plūs et Minus

Solve these arithmetic problems. Then change the words to Roman numerals.

1. ūnus plūs duo sunt _____ *trēs* _____ *I + II = III*

2. quattuor plūs quīnque sunt _____ _____

3. octō minus sex sunt _____ _____

4. trēs plūs septem sunt _____ _____

24

5. sex minus duo sunt        _____    _____

6. novem minus ūnus sunt     _____    _____

7. duo multiplicātum per trēs sunt    _____    _____

8. decem dīvīsum per duo sunt    _____    _____

# Roman Calendar

Iānuārius est prīmus mēnsis.
Februārius est secundus mēnsis.
Martius est tertius mēnsis.
Aprīlis est quārtus mēnsis.
Māius est quīntus mēnsis.
Iūnius est sextus mēnsis.
Iūlius est septimus mēnsis.
Augustus est octāvus mēnsis.
September est nōnus mēnsis.
Octōber est decimus mēnsis.
November est ūndecimus mēnsis.
December est duodecimus mēnsis.

As you can see, the names of our months come from the Roman calendar.

The Roman year used to begin with the month of **Martius** (March). For this reason, the *seventh* month was September, from **septem**. After January and February were added to the beginning of the year, September became the ninth month of the year instead of the seventh.

*November* is the eleventh month. How can you tell that **ūndec-imus** means "eleventh"? Hint: Divide the word into its two parts and add them together. *December* is the twelfth month. Explain how **duodecimus** means "twelfth."

The numbers that you see in front of the word **mēnsis** (month) are called *ordinal* numbers because they show the *order* of the months from first to twelfth. Give in Latin:

fourth month    *quārtus mēnsis*

second month    _____

eighth month    _____

first month    _____

Remember the story of the founding of Rome? Answer in Latin:

Quis est **prīmus** Rōmānus? _____

The ordinal numbers give us more root-forms for number words in English:

| prim- | second- | quart- | quint- | sext- | octav- | decim- |
|-------|---------|--------|--------|-------|--------|--------|
| I | II | IV | V | VI | VIII | X |

Here is a list of the most important Latin root-forms for 1 to 10. Next to each root is an example of an English word based on it:

I. **ūni-**    unit
    **prim-**    primary

II. **du-**    duet
    **bi-**    bicycle
    **second-**    secondary

III. **tri-**    triple

IV. **quadr-**    quadruped
    **quārt-**    quarter

V. **quint-**    quintet

VI. **sext-**    sextet

VII. **sept-**    September

VIII. **oct-**    octopus
    **octāv-**    octave

IX. **novem-**    November

X. **dec-**    decade
    **decim-**    decimal

Try these:

1. If a *sextet* is a group of six, how many members make up a *quartet*? _____.

A group of five is a _____. A group of seven is a _____.

A group of eight is an _____. A group of two is a _____.

2. Remember the *foot* root-forms **pod-** and **ped-**? Another root-form for *foot* is **pus-**.

Now give the root meaning of *octopus*: _____ + _____.
**Poly-** means "many." The Romans called an octopus a **polypus**. Why?

3. **Prīm-** can mean "highest" as well as "first." A *prima ballerina* in a dance company is not a beginner. She's the best dancer, the one who is first, the star. On the other hand, *primary school* is the first school you attend but not the highest. In fact, *secondary school* (high school) is higher than primary school. Since you attend it later, after *primary* school, it's called *secondary* school.

## The Eights Have It

OCTAVE OCTAGON OCTET OCTOBER OCTOPUS OCTOGENARIAN

1. Eight musicians playing together form an _____.

2. When the Roman calendar had ten months, the eighth was

_____.

3. "Do, Re, Mi, Fa, Sol, La, Ti, Do" makes a musical _____.

4. An eight-sided figure is an _____.

5. A marine animal with eight tentacles is called an _____.

6. Claudia's grandfather is 80 years old; he's an _____.

## Match It Up

1. septet          _____ a musical composition for three instruments
2. primate         _____ one of five babies born at the same time
3. decimate        _____ sounding as one, in agreement
4. trio            _____ a reciting of prayers for nine days in a row
5. unisonal        _____ a group of seven
6. duplicate       _____ one-fourth of a gallon
7. quintuplet      _____ to kill one in every ten
8. quart           _____ highest order of animal in biological classification
9. novena          _____ a copy or double

27

# LECTIŌ VI

# Deī Rōmānī

## Fābella: Ad Templum

**Persōnae:** Cornēlia, Lūcius, Claudia

Lucius and Claudia have had a great time showing their cousin Cornelia the sights of Rome. On her last morning in the city, Cornelia visits the *Temple of Jupiter Maximus* (The Greatest) on the Capitoline Hill. She admires the carved statues of Jupiter and other gods and goddesses at the top of the temple.

**CORNĒLIA:** (*looking at the large temple*) Templum est magnum! (*pointing to a statue*) Statua est magna! Quis est?

**CLAUDIA:** Iuppiter est. Iuppiter est rēx deōrum. Iuppiter est deus maximus.

**CORNĒLIA:** (*pointing to another statue*) Dea est. Quis est?

**LŪCIUS:** Iūnō est. Iūnō est rēgīna deōrum. Iūnō est dea maxima.

*The three cousins hurry back to the house so that Cornelia won't miss her carriage. Lucius and Claudia promise to visit Cornelia in the summer.*

**CORNĒLIA:** Tibi grātiās agō, Lūcī! Tibi grātiās agō, Claudia! Rōma est maxima! Rōma est optima! Rōmae habitāre volō. Valēte!

**LŪCIUS ET CLAUDIA:** (*waving*) Valē, Cornēlia! Valē, amīca!

---

### Vocabulary Help:

| | |
|---|---|
| rēx deōrum—king of the gods | rēgīna deōrum—queen of the gods |
| deus—god | optima—the best |
| dea—goddess | Rōmae habitāre volō—I want to live in Rome |

28

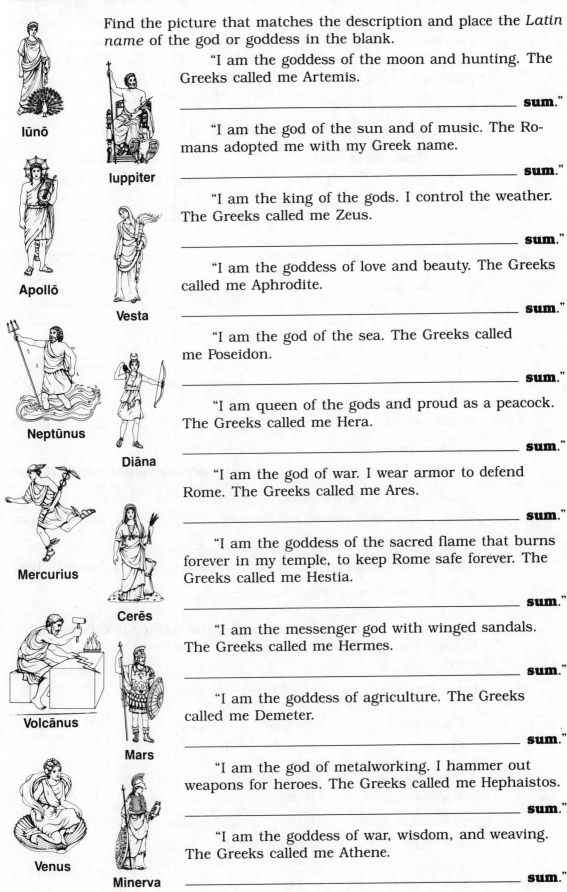

Find the picture that matches the description and place the *Latin name* of the god or goddess in the blank.

"I am the goddess of the moon and hunting. The Greeks called me Artemis.

_____ **sum.**"

"I am the god of the sun and of music. The Romans adopted me with my Greek name.

_____ **sum.**"

"I am the king of the gods. I control the weather. The Greeks called me Zeus.

_____ **sum.**"

"I am the goddess of love and beauty. The Greeks called me Aphrodite.

_____ **sum.**"

"I am the god of the sea. The Greeks called me Poseidon.

_____ **sum.**"

"I am queen of the gods and proud as a peacock. The Greeks called me Hera.

_____ **sum.**"

"I am the god of war. I wear armor to defend Rome. The Greeks called me Ares.

_____ **sum.**"

"I am the goddess of the sacred flame that burns forever in my temple, to keep Rome safe forever. The Greeks called me Hestia.

_____ **sum.**"

"I am the messenger god with winged sandals. The Greeks called me Hermes.

_____ **sum.**"

"I am the goddess of agriculture. The Greeks called me Demeter.

_____ **sum.**"

"I am the god of metalworking. I hammer out weapons for heroes. The Greeks called me Hephaistos.

_____ **sum.**"

"I am the goddess of war, wisdom, and weaving. The Greeks called me Athene.

_____ **sum.**"

Iūnō

Iuppiter

Apollō

Vesta

Neptūnus

Diāna

Mercurius

Cerēs

Volcānus

Mars

Venus

Minerva

**29**

The *English* spelling of the names of the Roman deities (gods and goddesses) is sometimes different from the Latin spelling:

| | | | | | |
|---|---|---|---|---|---|
| Jupiter | Juno | Apollo | Diana | Mercury | Vesta |
| Vulcan | Ceres | Neptune | Venus | Mars | Minerva |

Fill in the charts below with the English and Latin names.

| Deae Rōmānae | | Deī Rōmānī | |
|---|---|---|---|
| **English** | **Latin** | **English** | **Latin** |
| *Juno* | *Jūnō* | _____ | _____ |
| _____ | _____ | _____ | _____ |
| _____ | _____ | _____ | _____ |
| _____ | _____ | _____ | _____ |
| _____ | _____ | _____ | _____ |
| _____ | _____ | _____ | _____ |

What happens to the Latin letter *I* in the English names? It changes to _____.

In which chart are most of the English and Latin spellings the same, the chart of the **deae** or of the **deī**? _____.

What is the Latin ending on the names of three *gods* that changes or disappears in English? _____.

What is the Latin ending on the names of three *goddesses* that stays the same in English? _____.

For each pair of names below, put **S** if the spelling of the Latin and English *ending* stays the same, **D** if the *ending* changes or disappears.

| Latin Name | English Name | **S** *or* **D** |
|---|---|---|
| Claudia | Claudia | _____ |
| Lūcius | Lucius | _____ |
| Aemilia | Emily | _____ |
| Marcus | Mark | _____ |
| Maria | Marie | _____ |
| Antōnius | Anthony | _____ |
| Iūlius | Julius | _____ |

As each of the eight planets in our solar system (besides Earth) was discovered by scientists, it received the name of a Roman deity.

Fill in the four planets named after gods we have already studied:

1. _____   2. _____   3. _____   4. _____

Fill in the planet named after a goddess. 5. _____

The three remaining planets are named after other gods:

**Sāturnus**, a very ancient Roman god identified with the Greek god Kronos, father of Jupiter. He had a huge temple at one end of the Forum, directly below the Temple of Jupiter on the Capitoline Hill. Part of the temple is still standing today. 6. _____

**Plūtō**, god of the underworld and brother of Neptune and Jupiter. He ruled over dead souls below the earth. His Greek name was Hades. 7. _____

**Ūranus**, a Greek sky god who was adopted by the Romans. He was Jupiter's grandfather. 8. _____

The planets revolve around the *sun*. They belong to the *solar* system. What's the connection? The English word *sun* is from the German **Sonne**, which means "sun." The English word *solar is* from the Latin **sol**, which means "sun." Sometimes the Romans called the God of the Sun **Sol** instead of **Apollo**!

## Word Play

Fill in the blanks with the following words:

VOLCANIC     MERCURIAL     MARTIAL     CEREAL     JOVIAL

1. If you're speedy like Mercury, you're _____.

2. If you're made of grain which Ceres causes to grow, you're

   _____.

3. If you learn how to fight like the god Mars, you study

   _____ arts.

4. If you're heated up like Vulcan's furnace, you're _____ rock.

5. If you're merry like Jove (another name for Jupiter), you're

   _____.

# Review I

## Vērum aut Falsum?

Here are twelve sentences in Latin. Find the **six** that are *true* and put an X next to each. Then translate the *true* sentences in the spaces provided. The first one is done for you.

1. __X__ Claudia est puella Rōmāna.

2. _____ Lūcius est puer Rōmānus.

3. _____ Lūcius est discipula.

4. _____ Cornēlia est puer.

5. _____ Rōmulus est prīmus Rōmānus.

6. _____ Iānuārius est secundus mēnsis.

7. _____ Ūnus plūs sex sunt septem.

8. _____ Duo multiplicātum per quīnque sunt octō.

9. _____ Quattuor dīvīsum per duo sunt trēs.

10. _____ Novem minus quattuor sunt quīnque.

11. _____ Italia est in Āfricā.

12. _____ Rōma est in Italiā.

1. _____ *Claudia is a Roman girl.* _____

_____

_____

_____

_____

# Quis Sum?

**Augustus**

**ōrātius**

**Aenēas**

**ōmulus**

**Iūlius Caesar**

**s Scaevola**

Match the name of each famous character with the event:

1. "I founded the city of Rome. **Quis sum**?" "_____ es."

2. "I burned my right hand to prove Romans are brave. **Quis sum**?" "_____ es."

3. "I was so great and powerful that my fellow citizens murdered me. **Quis sum**?" "_____ es."

4. "I held off a whole army by myself on a bridge. **Quis sum**?" "_____ es."

5. "I landed in Italy with the help of my mother Venus. **Quis sum**?" "_____ es."

6. "I was the first emperor of Rome. **Quis sum**?" "_____ es."

# Quid Est?

Place the number of the famous sight in Rome next to its description:

1. Colosseum
2. Circus Maximus
3. Forum Romanum
4. Bath of Trajan
5. Pantheon
6. Theater of Marcellus
7. Palatine Hill

_____ the center of business and government activity

_____ a place for cleansing, exercise, and relaxation

_____ a wealthy district of Rome

_____ a large amphitheater for gladiatorial contests

_____ the largest course for chariot races

_____ a building admired for its huge dome

_____ place where plays were performed

33

# Deī et Deae

Pick the letter of the choice in Column B that best describes the god or goddess in Column A.

| Column A | | Column B |
|---|---|---|
| 1. Iuppiter | _____ | a. Queen of the gods |
| 2. Iūnō | _____ | b. God of the sea |
| 3. Apollō | _____ | c. Goddess of agriculture |
| 4. Cerēs | _____ | d. King of the gods |
| 5. Minerva | _____ | e. Goddess of wisdom and weaving |
| 6. Mercurius | _____ | f. God of war |
| 7. Diāna | _____ | g. Goddess of love |
| 8. Mars | _____ | h. God of metalworking and weapons |
| 9. Venus | _____ | i. Goddess of the flame in the temple |
| 10. Neptūnus | _____ | j. God of the sun and music |
| 11. Vesta | _____ | k. Goddess of the moon and hunting |
| 12. Volcānus | _____ | l. Messenger god |

# Cross It Out!

Cross out the *one* item in each list that does not belong with the others.

1. Romance languages: French, Spanish, German, Italian, Portuguese
2. Nations in the Roman Empire: Italia, Gallia, Aegyptus, China, Hispānia
3. English words from **ūni-**: unite, unique, under, unicorn, unicycle
4. Roman numerals: X, I, V, Q, C
5. People in the Forum: shoppers, senators, soldiers, acrobats, movie stars
6. City life in ancient Rome: crowds, fast food, street lights, noise, buildings

7. Latin words describing people: **magistra, camera, discipula, puella, fēmina**

# Number Exchange

Fill in the blanks:

1. If a duet is a group of *two*, a quartet is a group of _____, and a quintet is a group of _____. What is the word for a group of *eight*? It is an _____.

2. Although people are *bipeds*, many animals are *quadrupeds* because they have _____.

3. If a person speaks *two* languages, she is bilingual. If she speaks *three* languages, she is _____.

4. If a biennial event takes place every *two* years, a triennial event takes place every _____ years, and a quadrennial event every _____ years.

5. A quadrangle is a shape with *four* angles. What is the word for a shape with *three* angles? _____.

6. If triplets are *three* babies born at the same time, quintuplets are _____ babies born at the same time, and quadruplets are _____ babies born at the same time.

7. If October used to be the *eighth* month in the Roman calendar, November was the _____ month. What was the *tenth* month called? _____.

8. How many wheels does a bicycle have? _____
   Add *cycle* to the Latin root-forms for *one* and *three* to make two more *cycle* words in English: one-wheeler _____, three-wheeler _____.

Each branch of this Latin number tree contains English words from Latin roots. Find the *correct* English word to complete each sentence below. You will not use all the choices.

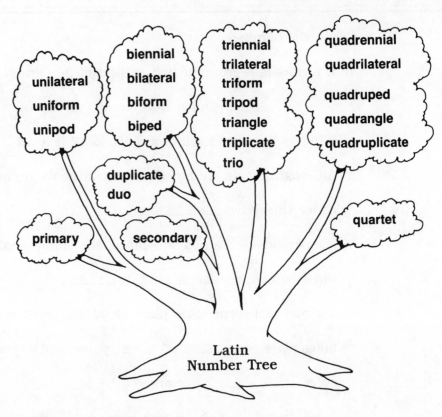

Latin
Number Tree

1. The first school you attend is called _____ school.

2. Four people playing music together make up a _____.

3. If a trio is a group of three, a group of two is a _____.

4. Because it has only one foot, a clam is called a _____.

5. An event that takes place every three years is _____.

6. A figure with four angles is called a _____.

7. If cookies have one size and shape, they are _____.

8. If you make three copies of a letter, you copy it in _____.

9. A peace treaty signed by two sides is a _____ agreement.

10. A person who can change his shape into that of a wolf is _____.

# Part
# TWO
# *Familia Claudī*

In this unit, you will:

meet the family of Claudius, a Roman senator
meet Quintus, a freedman
look inside a Roman house and apartment building
discuss slavery and freedom in Rome
describe yourself and your family in Latin
sing a Latin song about the family
perform a Roman ceremony in Latin
read a Latin story
learn many English words that come from Latin

# LECTIŌ VII

# Familia Claudī I

## Family Members

Here are the four members of Claudius' immediate family. Fill in the blanks. Choose your answers from the following list:

**puer   puella   vir   fēmina   soror**
**pater   māter   frāter   fīlius   fīlia**

Lūcius est _____.

Lūcius est _____.

Lūcius est _____.

**Lūcius**

Claudius est _____.

Claudius est _____.

**Claudius**

Antōnia est _____.

Antōnia est _____.

**Antōnia**

Claudia est _____.

Claudia est _____.

Claudia est _____.

**Claudia**

## The Roman Family

The English word *family* comes from the Latin word **familia**, which means "household." The **paterfamiliās** (father of the household) was in charge of his own **familia**, and he had absolute power. In addition to the immediate family members, the **familia** would include slaves, other relatives, and anyone else who depended on the **paterfamiliās**. When a son became an adult or got married, he might leave his father's household and begin a new one. After a daughter married, she joined the **familia** of her new husband.

There were many types of households in ancient Rome, just as there are many types of American families. Here are three Roman households. As you read, compare the life-styles and responsibilities of the Roman family members with those of your own.

38

## Familia Egnātī

**Pater**: "**Egnātius sum**. I work long hours in a bakery to support my family. My wife, two sons, two daughters, and I live in rooms behind my shop."

**Māter**: "**Aurēlia sum**. I help my husband in his bakery but spend most of my time taking care of my family's needs: their food and clothing."

**Fīlius Prīmus**: "**Marcus sum**. My father sends my brother and me to a teacher every morning to learn how to read and write. He teaches us how to bake bread in the afternoons."

**Fīlius Secundus**: "**Gāius sum**. I wear a tunic all day now. When I'm about 16, I'll receive the white toga that only grown men may wear."

**Fīlia Prīma**: "**Egnātia sum**. I am 14 years old. Father and mother will choose a husband for me soon. Father has been saving money for my dowry."

**Fīlia Secunda**: "**Egnātia Secunda sum**. I spend all day with mother. She teaches me sewing, weaving, cooking, and all the things I must know to be a good wife."

## Familia Pūblicī

**Paterfamiliās**: "**Pūblicius sum**. My household is very large, with my wife, children, their families, and many slaves. We live in a large house in the city and spend summers in a villa in the country."

**Wife of Paterfamiliās**: "**Cassia sum**. I spend my days managing the household. I direct the slaves as they clean, shop, and cook."

**Pater**: "**Servius Pūblicius sum**. I am a wealthy young man, married ten years. I live in my parents' house, where my father, the **paterfamiliās**, is the absolute authority over me and my own family."

**Māter**: "**Iūlia Pūblicia sum**. When I married ten years ago, I took my husband's name and became part of his household. I help my mother-in-law with the slaves."

**Fīlius**: "**Sextus sum**. I want to be a public official, like my grandfather. I'll have to study public speaking and Roman law."

**Fīlia**: "**Pūblicia sum**. I stay with my mother and grandmother most of the day and watch them directing the slaves. I play games with my friends. I have many dolls."

## Familia Marī

**Paterfamiliās**: "**Marius sum**. I am a banker in Rome. I take care of financial matters for my sons. When I die, each son will start his own household."

**Māter**: "**Octāvia sum**. The banker is my third husband. My parents selected my first husband, but the marriage didn't last. My second husband was a soldier and was killed in battle."

**Fīlius Prīmus**: "**Brūtus sum**. I'm married and have three children of my own. Father has put me in charge of the farmlands he owns outside the city."

**Fīlius Secundus**: "**Spurius sum**. I live with my mother and stepfather. My real father was a brave soldier who was killed in a great battle. The banker adopted me as his own son."

**Fīlia**: "**Maria sum**. My parents send me to a teacher each morning. Most of the other students are boys, but I think girls should know how to read and write too."

**Avunculus (Brother of Māter)**: "**Quīntus Octāvius sum**. I live with my sister and her husband, the banker. I invested much money in shiploads of merchandise that were stolen by pirates."

**Fīlia of Avunculus**: "**Octāvia sum**. My father and I are living with my aunt until my father can earn enough to buy us a house. My aunt takes good care of me."

---

### Questions to Think About

1. Who, according to Roman law, was responsible for a family? Is this true today?
2. How did the different family members (**pater, māter, fīlius, fīlia**) spend their time? How does this compare with family members today?
3. Did Roman children have to attend school? Who decided? Is this true today?

1. Words belong to groups just as people belong to families. Fill in the answers to the following questions to make one word group:

   If *maternal* means "motherly, like a mother," what does *paternal* mean? *Paternal* means _____.

   How do you say "brotherly, like a brother"? _____.

   Think of the Latin word for *sister*. How do you say "sisterly"?

   (Hint: Leave out the *n* this time) _____.

   Here is another word group to make:

   If *maternity* means "motherhood," what does *paternity* mean?

   *Paternity* means _____.

   *Fraternity* means _____.

   *Sorority* means _____.

   You may know other meanings for *fraternity* and *sorority*. See if you can connect them with the basic meaning you put in the blanks.

2. To form word groups, we take the Latin root-form and add an ending to it. The endings we added above are **-al** and **-ity**. There are many other endings for the roots we have learned. For each word in the left column below, fill in a comparable word in the right column:

   | pater, patr- | māter, mātr- |
   | --- | --- |
   | paterfamilias | *materfamilias* |
   | patriarch | _____ |
   | patron | *matron* |
   | patrimony | _____ |

   It is easy to see the spelling relationship between each word pair. But what do the words mean? As you discuss these words with your teacher, keep in mind a major difference between the father and the mother in the Roman family: The father held the power and money, while the mother cared for the children at home. Do the meanings of the modern English words in the chart illustrate this difference between male and female roles? Consider this: If a woman gives money to a museum, she becomes a *patron*, a person with the power of the **pater**!

# Familia Claudī II

## Slavery in Ancient Rome

In the United States, the word *slavery* brings to mind the difficult period before the Civil War, when people from Africa were bought and sold by slave-traders, mostly to work on farms, where they were often treated badly. In ancient times, for *millions* of people all over the Mediterranean world, slavery was very common. The Romans considered it a normal and acceptable part of life. There were many kinds of slaves, and they had an, important role in the everyday activities of the city. Try to keep this idea in mind as you learn about slavery in ancient Rome.

### How Many Slaves Were in a Familia?

Mopsus and Amabilis were part of the **familia** of Claudius. Since Claudius was a middle-class man, he would have at least 20 or 30 slaves in his city house. Even a very poor man often owned at least one slave. A wealthy man might keep a city house with 200 slaves and several farms with hundreds more. During the Roman Empire, the number of slaves in Rome was very large—about half of the total population.

### How Did a Person Become a Slave?

Slaves were sent to the city of Rome from all parts of the Empire. They were usually ordinary people who were taken prisoner by the conquering Roman army or by pirates. There were slaves of both sexes and all ages. Some were highly educated or skilled in a trade. The enormous Roman Empire included peoples from many different countries and races. When prisoners came to Rome as slaves, they had to leave behind their families, their jobs, and the language and customs of their native country. They were forced to adjust to the Roman style of life.

## What Rights Did Slaves Have?

Prisoners were sold in slave markets by slave-traders. Once they were bought, they became the property of their master. They had no legal rights. They could not marry, vote, or wear the toga of citizenship. Their children were born into slavery and belonged to the master. If a slave tried to escape, he might be branded on his forehead with the letters FUG, short for **fugitivus**, which means "runaway."

Some masters were quite cruel to their slaves, while others were considerate and kind. Since slaves needed to be properly fed, dressed, and rested in order to work well, it would be foolish for a master to harm his slaves and make them unfit for their tasks. Slaves usually lived in the same house as the master and his family. Although they weren't free, sometimes these household slaves became very close to the family and over the years were treated with affection.

## What Did Slaves Do?

Slaves did all kinds of work. Country slaves worked the land owned by their master. Their life was hard—they worked long hours in the fields. Slaves living in the city house worked in teams with specific duties—cleaning, cooking, child care, clothing. Others were personal family attendants, going everywhere with their masters or mistresses. Still others might work in factories, teach school, make handcrafted objects, take care of the city parks, or become actors and musicians. The very strongest were sometimes trained as gladiators.

As they worked, slaves mingled with free men. They went shopping, attended shows in the theater, and participated in religious festivals at the temples. They did not wear special clothes. A foreigner visiting Rome would not be able to tell the slaves apart from the poor, free working men. Slaves blended into the business and life of the great city.

### Time Traveler: A Slave in Rome

Imagine you are from a foreign country which has been conquered by the Romans. You have just been sent to Rome to be sold at auction as a slave. Describe your feelings, the life you left behind, the master who buys you, and what kind of life you can expect. Write your story on a separate piece of paper.

43

1. You have seen that one Latin root gives us many English words. **Servus/serva, serv-** is a good example. Fill in the chart to see how:

| Latin Word and Root | English Word | Meaning of the English Word |
|---|---|---|
| servus/serva serv- | _____ | _____ |
| | _____ | _____ |
| | _____ | _____ |
| | _____ | _____ |
| | _____ | _____ |
| | _____ | _____ |
| | _____ | _____ |
| | _____ | _____ |

2. Add the following English word to the **-al** word group: *filial*, from **filius/filia, fili-**, "like a son or daughter." The name of the family dog, Rex, means "king." From the Latin word **rēx, rēg-** we get English *regal*. Notice the **-al** ending. What do you think *regal* means?
   It means "like a _____."

3. The ending **-ine** means the same thing as **-al**, "related to" or "like." It is used with Latin roots for animal names. For example, *canine* means "like a dog," from **canis, can-**. Think of Bella. What does *feline* mean? To make the English word, add **-ine** to the root. Try these:

| Latin | English | |
|---|---|---|
| canis, can- *dog* | *canine* | like a dog |
| leō, leōn- *lion* | _____ | like a lion |
| asinus, asin- *donkey* | _____ | like a donkey |
| porcus, porc- *pig* | _____ | like a pig |
| aquila, aquil- *eagle* | _____ | like an eagle |

This is a Roman temple in the Doric style. Lucius and Claudia want to climb the stairs to the top. You can help them by marking the answers to the sentences either TRUE or FALSE.

_____ 1. The male leader of a tribe is known as the *matriarch*.

_____ 2. Mothers-to-be often buy clothes in *maternity* shops.

_____ 3. Slaves always have *regal* living quarters.

_____ 4. At colleges some young men join *sororities*.

_____ 5. *Fraternal* feelings are the feelings Lucius had for Claudia.

_____ 6. Lions, tigers, and cougars are *felines*.

_____ 7. A *patron* of a store has the money to buy something in it.

_____ 8. Your father's sister is your *maternal* relative.

_____ 9. A person who is *servile* in manner is probably a king.

_____ 10. *Canine* teeth are sharp and pointed like a dog's teeth.

_____ 11. Before the Civil War, slaves were in a condition of *servitude*.

_____ 12. To identify the *paternity* of a new litter of puppies, you have to discover which dog was the father.

Now that you have answered all the questions, you will find out if the children reached the top. For every answer that you marked TRUE, move UP *two* steps. For every answer you marked FALSE, move DOWN *one* step. There were nine steps. DID THEY MAKE IT?

# Quīntus Lībertus

## Language Discovery

Here are sentences you have heard in class. Write the translation of each in the space provided.

Quīntus est lībertus.   *Quīntus is a freedman.*

Mopsus est servus.   _____

Try these:

Quīntus est vir.   _____

Mopsus est vir.   _____

Antōnia est fēmina.   _____

Amābilis est fēmina.   _____

Circle the translation of **est** in each English sentence above.

Here are new sentences. Write the translation of each:

Quīntus et Mopsus sunt virī.   _____

Antōnia et Amābilis sunt fēminae.   _____

Circle the translation of **sunt** in each English sentence above.

Fill in each sentence below with either **est** or **sunt**:

1. Claudius _____ pater.
2. Claudius et Lūcius _____ pater et fīlius.
3. Claudius et Quīntus _____ virī.
4. Claudia _____ puella.
5. Claudia et Lūcius _____ soror et frāter.
6. Claudia et Lūcius _____ fīliī (children).
7. Bella et Rēx _____ animālia.
8. Bella _____ fēlēs.

By now you have probably figured out that **est** (is) is used with one person or thing, and **sunt** (are) with more than one. Here's another way to say this: The word **est** is singular. The word **sunt** is plural.

Nouns—words that are labels for persons and things—are also singular and plural. For most nouns in English, simply add **s** to the singular. Fill in the chart:

| Singular | Plural |
|---|---|
| boy | *boys* |
| girl | _____ |
| cat | _____ |
| animal | _____ |

Sometimes the spelling changes when **s** is added. Fill in the chart:

| | |
|---|---|
| butterfly | *butterflies* |
| story | _____ |
| wife | *wives* |
| leaf | _____ |

The situation can get more complicated. Fill in the chart:

| | |
|---|---|
| man | *men* |
| woman | _____ |
| child | _____ |
| fish | _____ (CAREFUL!!) |
| deer | _____ |

Latin usually shows a difference in the endings between singular and plural nouns. Here are lists of nouns you know (look how many!), along with their plurals:

| 1 | | 2 | | 3 | |
|---|---|---|---|---|---|
| **Singular** | **Plural** | **Singular** | **Plural** | **Singular** | **Plural** |
| puella | puellae | puer | puerī | pater | patrēs |
| fēmina | fēminae | vir | virī | māter | mātrēs |
| līberta | lībertae | lībertus | līberti | frāter | frātrēs |
| fīlia | fīliae | fīlius | fīliī | soror | sorōrēs |
| serva | servae | servus | servī | canis | canēs |

What is the plural ending of the nouns in **Box 1**?

Write it here _____. Now pronounce the words in the box

What is the plural ending of the nouns in **Box 2**?

Write it here _____. Now pronounce the words in the box.

Many Latin nouns form their plurals as in **Box 3**. Some of these nouns are masculine, like **pater**, and some are feminine, like **māter**.

Write the plural ending here _____. Now pronounce the words.

**47**

Circle the word that correctly completes each sentence below:

1. Claudia est (puella, puellae).
2. Mopsus est (servus, servī).
3. Claudius et Antōnia sunt (parēns, parentēs).
4. Claudius est (parēns, parentēs).
5. Antōnia et Amābilis sunt (fēmina, fēminae).
6. Rēx est (canis, canēs).
7. Claudius et Quīntus sunt (vir, virī).
8. Mopsus et Amābilis sunt (servus, serva, servī).
9. Lūcius est (discipulus, discipulī).
10. Lūcius et _____ sunt (discipulus, discipulī).
          (your Latin name)

# Freedom at Last!

Imagine yourself as a Roman slave dreaming of freedom. There were several different reasons you might be set free. It was common for a **paterfamiliās** to free his older, loyal slaves when he died by making a statement in his will. A slave might buy his freedom by saving up his money—either the money he earned if he was allowed to work at a trade, or the allowance he would be given for good service to his master. If a slave performed a deed of heroism, or just worked hard and was loyal over the years, his master would free him out of respect. But a master could not legally grant freedom until the slave was 30 years old.

Once freed, a slave became a **lībertus**, a freedman (or **līberta**, freedwoman), and took part of the former master's name. If the master was a Roman citizen, the freed person, too, became a citizen. Although he and his children could not run for high public office, like citizens who were born free, his grandchildren would have the right to do so. The freedman was free to carry on his own business and continued to depend on his former master as his patron. Some freedmen were highly educated, others were fine craftsmen in the trade they learned while they were slaves. Some became very wealthy and famous. Rich or poor, freedmen mixed freely with both slaves and free-born citizens.

# Fābella: Manūmissiō Quīntī

Persōnae: Quīntus, Claudius, Assertor (Defender), Praetor (Judge), Amīcī Claudī (Friends of Claudius), Antōnia

PRAETOR: Praetor sum. Quis est? (*points to Quintus*)

ASSERTOR: Quīntus est. Quīntus nōn est servus Claudī.

PRAETOR: (*turning to Claudius*) Vērum est? Quīntus nōn est servus tuus?

CLAUDIUS: Vērum est.

PRAETOR: (*to Quintus*) Venī, Quīnte. (*Quintus approaches the praetor and kneels. The praetor taps him on the head with a rod.*) Es līber, Quīnte.

CLAUDIUS: (*to Quintus*) Gere pilleum, Quīnte. (*He puts the cap of freedom on Quintus' head. Quintus stands up.*)

AMĪCĪ CLAUDĪ: Quīntus est lībertus! Quīntus est lībertus!

QUĪNTUS: Sum lībertus. Tibi grātiās agō, domine (*shakes Claudius' hand*). Grātiās agō, domina (*shakes Antonia's hand*).

ANTŌNIA: Bonus es, Quīnte. Venīte, omnēs. Cēna magna domī est.

---

### Vocabulary Help:

nōn—not
servus Claudī—the slave of
   Claudius
Vērum est?—Is it true?
tuus—your
līber—free
gere pilleum—wear the **pilleus**

tibi grātiās ago—I thank you
domine—master
domina—mistress
bonus—a good man
omnēs—everybody
cēna magna—a big dinner
domī—at home

# Word Search: Familia Claudī

Find and circle the **Latin** words for the English words listed to the right. Words may go across, down, or on the diagonal, but they are never backward.

```
S F P U E R S
E I M A S P O
R L A R T U R
V I T E B E O
U I E X I L R
S E R V A L I
F E L E S A E
```

1. boy
2. girl
3. female slave
4. male slave
5. sister
6. father
7. mother
8. cat
9. "King"
10. children
   (son and daughter)

49

# Mini-Review II

## Quis Sum?

Identify the speaker in each of the following as **P—pater, M—mäter, FS—fīlius, FA—fīlia, S—servus or serva, or L—lībertus**

_____ 1. Pirates captured me, and now I'm being sold at an auction.

_____ 2. I am learning the skills for being a good wife from my mother.

_____ 3. After I go to school in the morning, I work in my father's bakery.

_____ 4. I have the power of life and death over each family member by law.

_____ 5. I put on the **pilleus** at the end of my manumission ceremony.

_____ 6. My husband is rich. I manage the household and direct the slaves.

_____ 7. I work hard in the fields. My master is very harsh.

_____ 8. I will be allowed to wear the toga of manhood soon.

_____ 9. Father is saving for my dowry and will choose my husband soon.

## Singular or Plural I

First fill in each sentence below with either **est** or **sunt**.
Then translate the sentence into English.

1. Antōnia _____ māter. _____

2. Mopsus et Amābilis _____ servī. _____

_____

3. Rēx _____ canis. _____

4. Claudia et Lūcius _____ soror et frāter. _____

_____

**50**

Circle the form of the noun that completes each sentence correctly.

1. Lūcius est (puer/puerī).

2. Līvia et Claudia sunt (amīca/amīcae).

3. Quīntus et Mopsus sunt (vir/virī).

4. Amābilis est (serva/servae).

5. Claudius et Antōnia sunt (parēns/parentēs).

6. (Antōnia/Antōnia et Amābilis) sunt fēminae.

## Word Power

Here are eight English words based on Latin words you have learned. Circle the Latin root-form in each.

CANINE          REGAL          MATRIMONY       PATERFAMILIAS
LIBERTY         FILIAL         SERVANT         FRATERNAL

Complete the following sentences using these words.

1. The millionaire lived like a king; he lived in _____ splendor.

2. The minister at the wedding said, "I join you in holy

    _____."

3. German shepherds are members of the _____ family.

4. The father who is the head of the household is the

    _____.

5. Lucius and Claudia treated their parents with _____ devotion.

6. At the manumission ceremony, Claudius gave Quintus his

    _____.

7. The tired old man hired a _____ to clean his house.

8. Lucius and his best friend Publius were like brothers; they had

    _____ feelings for each other.

# LECTIŌ X

# Domus Claudī

## In Domō

This is a cut-away picture of Claudius' house.

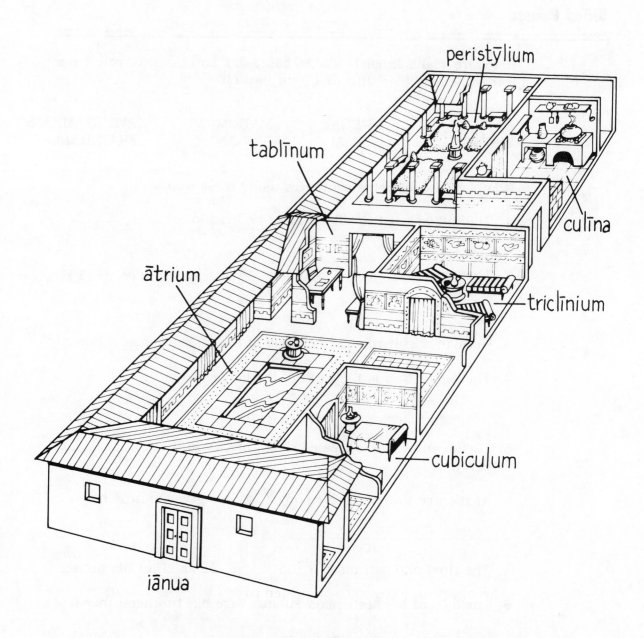

peristȳlium

tablīnum

culīna

ātrium

triclīnium

cubiculum

iānua

Fill in each blank below with the name of a room you see in the **domus**:

I am the main room of the house and the first room you enter. I have a small, shallow pool in my center to collect rainwater, which falls down from an opening in my ceiling directly above it. Although I have very little furniture, I am beautiful, with mosaic tiles on my floor and pictures of flowers, gods, and goddesses painted right on my walls. I have a few small windows high up, but sunlight shines in me from the roof opening. In one corner, I contain a small shrine with statues of the Claudian family gods for the **familia** to worship. Doorways covered with curtains lead from me to many rooms: at the front, to the shops my master rents out; at the sides, to the bedrooms; and in the back, to the family room, the dining room, and the hallway leading to the rest of the house.

**Quid sum**? _____

I am a very small room, but quite important. I contain a high wooden bed with a mattress stuffed with wool, an oil lamp, and a small dressing table. There is one small window high up in the wall. During the waking hours of the **familia**, I am never used, unless someone is sick.

**Quid sum**? _____

I am a popular room at dinner time. My walls are decorated with paintings of fruit and birds. I have a table in the middle, with *three* couches around it for people to lie on (re*cline*) while they eat.

**Quid sum**? _____

I am the family living room where only the **familia** and special friends are welcome. My master sits at a table and studies his account books or writes letters in me. My front entrance faces the **ātrium**, while my back opens on the garden at the back of the house.

**Quid sum**? _____

I am the large, airy courtyard at the back of the house. I am completely open, with a big garden (**hortus**) at my center filled with statues, flowers, and fresh herbs and spices. I am surrounded by fluted columns that hold up the roof for the rooms around my sides: the kitchen, the slaves' bedrooms, the bathroom, and storage rooms. Rex likes to sleep in me, especially on hot nights. In the summer, the family dines in me and relaxes with friends.

**Quid sum**? _____

I have a stove built against one wall and a large brick oven. Water enters my sink from underground pipes that connect up with the city water supply. My master pays for this hookup. Mopsus cooks in me.

**Quid sum**? _____

I. From the verb **habitat** come several English derivatives you may know. All have meanings connected to the meaning of the Latin stem, **habit-**: "live in," "dwell." Three are nouns (labels for things), one is a verb (action word), and four are adjectives (describing words). Here is a list:

| Nouns | Verbs | Adjectives |
|---|---|---|
| inhabitant | inhabit | inhabited |
| habitat | | uninhabited |
| habitation | | inhabitable |
| | | uninhabitable |

Fill in the blanks in the following four sentences with words from the **adjective** list, *without* looking up the meanings of the words in the dictionary. Look for hints in the sentences:

1. The new house is *able* to be lived *in*. It is _____.
2. The old house is *unable* to be lived *in*. It is _____.
3. The city house has a family living *in* it. It is _____.
4. The house in the ghost town is empty. It is _____.

Now match the **nouns** and the **verb** in the list at the top with their meanings:

1. A person who lives in a place is an _____.
2. The natural environment or living place of an animal is its _____.
3. Claudia's house is her place of _____.
4. To live in a place is to _____ it.

II. Did you know? A **dominus** is someone belonging to the **domus**, from **dom-**, meaning "house" + **-īnus**, meaning "related to." He's the master of the **domus**, or simply, the boss, the master. The name of the **dominus** of Mopsus and Amabilis is _____. A **domina** is the *mistress* of the **domus**.

The name of the slaves' **domina** is _____.

Translate silently: **Dominus et domina habitant in domō**. When you *dominate* a person, you act like a _____.

Fill in the chart with other English words from **domus**.

| | English Word | Meaning of English Word |
|---|---|---|
| **domus** (house) | | |
| dom- | _____ | |
| | _____ | |
| domin- | _____ | |
| | _____ | |

**1.** Here are some of the nouns you have learned about the house:

| 1 | 2 | 3 |
|---|---|---|
| culīn**a** | hort**us** | ātri**um** |
| iānua | mūrus | peristȳlium |
| fenestra | | tablīnum |
| mēnsa | | cubiculum |
| sella | | triclīnium |

Write two words for family members that have the same ending as the nouns in the first list: _____ _____.

Write the ending _____. Circle it in the list.

Write two words for family members that have the same ending as the nouns in the second list: _____ _____

Write the ending _____. Circle it in the list.

The third list is new. The common ending is _____. Circle it.

Like **serva, fīlia**, and **puella**, the nouns in List 1 are feminine.
Like **servus, fīlius**, and **puer**, the nouns in List 2 are masculine.

You might ask, "How can a *door* be feminine?
In Latin, and in *all* the Romance languages that come from it, every noun is assigned a category, called **gender**:

    Nouns ending in **-us** are usually *masculine* (*m*).
    Nouns ending in **-a** are usually *feminine* (*f*).
    Nouns ending in **-um** are *neuter* (Latin for *neither*—neither masculine nor feminine!) (*n*)

Here are some new nouns. Label them *m, f,* or *n*.

**lectus** (bed) _____     **larārium** (family shrine) _____
**lātrīna** (bathroom) _____     **vīlla** (country house) _____
**tēctum** (roof) _____     **impluvium** (pool for rainwater) _____

**2.** You now know the Latin words (nouns) for things around the house and the people who live in the house, and you also know how to group them. The next step is to find a way to describe these people and these items.

A word that describes a noun is called an **adjective**. Some English adjectives are: *pretty, ugly, kind, cowardly, big, little, angry, happy*. Write three more: _____.

Write a sentence in English describing each room in the Roman house. Use two adjectives in your sentence. Underline each. For example: The atrium is <u>large</u> and <u>beautiful</u>.

    *or*, The atrium has <u>beautiful</u> pictures and <u>small</u> windows.

# Īnsula Quīntī

## Language Discovery

Compare these sentences in English and Latin:

| | |
|---|---|
| The garden is <u>large</u>. | Hortus est <u>magnus</u>. |
| The kitchen is <u>large</u>. | Culīna est <u>magna</u>. |
| The atrium is <u>large</u>. | Ātrium est <u>magnum</u>. |

The adjectives are underlined in the three sentences.

What happens to the adjective in English? *It stays the same.*

What happens to the adjective in Latin? _____

**Magnus, magna**, and **magnum** are different forms of the same adjective with the base **magn-**, meaning "large." Only the *ending* changes.

Why does the ending change?
In Latin, adjectives and the nouns they describe are *partners*.
If the noun is *masculine* like **hortus**, so is the adjective—**magnus**.
If the noun is *feminine* like **culīna**, so is the adjective—**magna**.
If the noun is *neuter* like **ātrium**, so is the adjective—**magnum**.

Complete these sentences by circling the correct form of the Latin adjective, and then translate the sentence into English:

Vīlla est (magnus, (magna,) magnum).

_____ *The country house is large* _____.

Mūrus est (magnus, magna, magnum).

_____.

Peristȳlium est (magnus, magna, magnum).

_____.

**Some Latin Adjectives:**

magn**us**, magn**a**, magn**um**—large
parvus, parva, parvum—small
longus, longa, longum—long, tall
lātus, lāta, lātum—wide
altus, alta, altum—grown-up; high, deep
rīdiculus, rīdicula, rīdiculum—funny
pulcher, pulchra, pulchrum—beautiful
īrātus, īrāta, īrātum—angry

astūtus, astūta, astūtum—clever
stultus, stulta, stultum—stupid
bonus, bona, bonum—good
malus, mala, malum—bad
amīcus, amīca, amīcum—friendly
laetus, laeta, laetum—happy
trīst**is** (m), trīst**is** (f), trīst**e** (n)—sad
dēformis, dēformis, dēforme—ugly

Choose any *five* nouns you know (names of rooms, people, or classroom objects). Pick an adjective from the list above to describe each noun and use the two in a Latin sentence. You can do it!
Here are some examples:

Peristȳlium est lātum.
Servus est bonus.
Amābilis est pulchr**a**. (Remember, she is feminine.)
Pater est alt**us**. (Remember, **pater** is masculine.)

# Legāmus!

## Flammae!

| | |
|---|---|
| Claudius et Antōnia habitant in domō. | (1) |
| Amābilis et Mopsus habitant in domō. | (2) |
| Quīntus in domō nōn habitat. In īnsulā habitat. Quīntus est | (3) |
| lībertus. | (4) |
| Post merīdiem Quīntus ambulat in viā ad īnsulam. | (5) |
| Laetus est quod sōl lūcet. Lībertus cantat et ambulat. | (6) |
| Subitō Quīntus fūmum videt. Flammās videt. | (7) |
| Flammae sunt magnae et altae. | (8) |
| "Flammae! Flammae!" clāmat Quīntus. | (9) |
| Vigilēs aquam portant. Flammās exstinguunt. | (10) |
| Quīntus est fortūnātus. Īnsula tūta est. | (11) |

*Vocabulary Help:*

(5) post merīdiem—in the afternoon
　　ambulat—is walking
　　viā—street
　　ad īnsulam—near his apartment block
(6) laetus—happy
　　quod—because
　　sōl lūcet—the sun is shining
(7) subitō—suddenly
　　fūmum—smoke

　　videt—sees
　　flammās—flames
(8) magnae—large
　　altae—high
(9) clāmat—shouts
(10) vigilēs—firemen
　　aquam—water
　　portant—carry
　　exstinguunt—they extinguish
(11) fortūnātus—lucky, fortunate
　　tūta—safe

### Respondē Latīnē:

1. Ubi ambulat Quīntus?
2. Cūr (why) est Quīntus laetus?
3. Quid videt Quīntus? Quid clāmat?

4. Quī portant aquam?
5. Cūr est Quīntus fortūnātus?

**57**

1. **Īnsula** (island) is the source of some important English words:

   *insulate*: to seal off
   *insulated*: sealed off
   *insulation*: material used to seal something off

   The carpenter was hired to _____ the house.

   He used _____ inside the walls to protect the house from the cold.

   The house is now cozy and warm because it is _____.

   Think about it: When we wrap ourselves in a blanket, we are like an island, completely surrounded. We are *insulated* or protected from the outside.

   Did you know? Italy is a *peninsula*, from Latin **paene** (almost) + **insula**. Italy is an "almost island." Look at the map on p. 8 to see why!

2. The English noun ending -**itude** is used with some of the adjectives you have learned. For example, **altus** (high) from the root **alt-** + **-itude** = *altitude*:

   *When you fly in a plane, the pilot announces its* altitude *or height.*

   Here are some more **-itude** words. See how many you recognize or can figure out from the meaning of the Latin adjective.

   *magnitude, longitude, latitude, pulchritude*

3. The English verb ending **-ify** means "to make": *magnify* means "to make large."

   What do these verbs mean?

   *beautify, stultify, verify* (**vēr-** means "true")

4. Some Latin adjectives in the list on p. 57 give English adjectives that mean the same as the Latin and are spelled almost exactly the same as the Latin. Figure out the meaning of these English adjectives:

   irate _____          ridiculous _____

   astute _____          deformed _____

5. Match the Latin adjective with the English word that comes from it:

   1. bonus    4. longus    _____ magnificent    _____ amicable

   2. malus    5. amīcus    _____ prolong    _____ malicious

   3. magnus              _____ bonanza

58

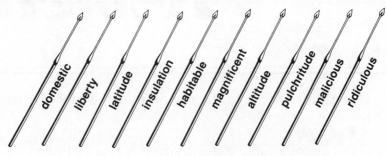

## *Javelin Contest*

Help Romulus win the javelin contest. Complete each of the sentences below with a word from the list above.

1. A dog can be trained to live in a house; dogs are _____ animals.

2. It would be dangerous if an airplane pilot got dizzy at a high _____.

3. You can locate your city on a map if you know its longitude and _____.

4. When the slave was set free, he enjoyed his _____.

5. Beautiful Miss Piggy thinks she is an example of feminine _____.

6. The Romans did not have electricity, but their houses were _____.

7. The bad witch designed a _____ plan to kill Hansel and Gretel.

8. A goose-feather filled coat is very good _____ against the cold.

9. Trimalchio owned a very large and fancy house; it was _____.

10. Lucius laughed at Claudia; she looked _____ in her Juno costume.

Score 2 points for each correct answer. Romulus needed at least 14 points to win. DID HE SUCCEED?

# Review II

## Quis est . . . ?

Mark an *X* next to the nouns that describe the character.

**Example:**

Lūcius est. . .    _X_ 1. puer    _X_ 2. fīlius    ___ 3. pater

___ 4. soror    _X_ 5. frāter    _X_ 6. discipulus

Claudia est. . .    ___ 1. soror    ___ 2. puella    ___ 3. fīlia

___ 4. puer    ___ 5. māter    ___ 6. frāter

Claudius est. . .    ___ 1. frāter    ___ 2. dominus    ___ 3. parēns

___ 4. pater    ___ 5. servus    ___ 6. vir

Rēx est. . .    ___ 1. fēlēs    ___ 2. puella    ___ 3. animal

___ 4. canis    ___ 5. dominus    ___ 6. amīcus

Antōnia et Claudius sunt. . .

___ 1. parēns    ___ 2. parentēs    ___ 3. virī

___ 4. vir et fēmina    ___ 5. dominī    ___ 6. pater et māter

Quīntus et Mopsus sunt. . .

___ 1. servī    ___ 2. lībertus et servus    ___ 3. virī

___ 4. puerī    ___ 5. frāter et soror    ___ 6. dominī

## Ubi Sum?

Match the description and the place in the Roman house.

| | |
|---|---|
| ___ 1. culīna | a. small room for sleeping |
| ___ 2. ātrium | b. room with three couches and a table |
| ___ 3. cubiculum | c. open courtyard in back of house |
| ___ 4. triclīnium | d. private family room and study |
| ___ 5. peristȳlium | e. bathroom |
| ___ 6. hortus | f. pool for rainwater |
| ___ 7. lātrīna | g. kitchen |
| ___ 8. tablīnum | h. garden |
| ___ 9. impluvium | i. main room in the front of the house |

# Crossword Puzzle

Clues: PERISTŸLIŌ   PATER
       RĒX           FAMILIA
       ĀTRIUM     DOMŌ
       MĀTER      ĪNSULĀ

1. Lūcius et Claudia habitant in_____.

2. Antōnia est _____.

3. _____ Claudī habitat in domō.

4. _____ est magnum.

5. Hortus est in _____.

6. Quīntus habitat in_____.

7. Claudius est _____.

8. _____ est canis.

# Roman Life-styles

Put an X next to each statement that is TRUE.

1. _____ A slave's treatment depended primarily on the master.

2. _____ **Familia** is the Latin word for household or family.

3. _____ Roman children were required by law to attend school.

4. _____ Roman women had the same legal rights as American women.

5. _____ A slave might be able to buy his or her own freedom.

6. _____ Rich Roman households might have as many as 200 city slaves.

7. _____ Romans always sat up straight while they dined.

8. _____ A Roman house was organized around the **ātrium** and the **peristȳlium**.

9. _____ A freedman could hold high political office.

10. _____ The Latin word for apartment block, **insula**, also means "island."

**61**

## Ad Mare

| | |
|---|---|
| Pūblius est frāter Līviae et amīcus Lūcī. | (1) |
| Lūcius et Pūblius ambulant ad mare. | (2) |
| Claudia et Līvia quoque ambulant ad mare. | (3) |
| Quattuor līberī in aquā natant. Aqua est salsa et frīgida. | (4) |
| Pūblius laetus nōn est. Puer timidus ex aquā exit. | (5) |
| Lūcius laetus in aquā natat et lūdit. | (6) |
| Puellae laetae in aquā natant et lūdunt. | (7) |
| Subitō polypus pedem Lūcī capit. Puer clāmat, "Fer auxilium!" | (8) |
| Duae puellae puerum līberant. | (9) |
| "Multās grātiās!" Lūcius inquit. "Estis puellae bonae et fortēs." | (10) |

---

### Vocabulary Help:

(1) frāter Līviae—Livia's brother
amīcus Lūcī—a friend of
Lucius
(2) ambulant—are walking
ad mare—near the sea
(3) quoque—also
(4) līberī—children
in aquā—in the water
natant—are swimming
salsa—salty
frīgida—cold
(5) laetus nōn est—isn't happy
timidus—frightened
ex aquā exit—leaves the water

(6) lūdit—is playing
(8) subitō—suddenly
polypus—octopus
pedem Lūcī capit—grabs the
foot of Lucius
clāmat—shouts
Fer auxilium!—Help!
(9) puerum līberant—free the
boy
(10) multās grātiās—many
thanks!
inquit—says
estis—you are
fortēs—brave

# Respondē Latīnē

1. Quis est Pūblius?
2. Ubi ambulant līberī?
3. Cūr (Why) nōn est Pūblius laetus?
4. Quid capit polypus?
5. Quae puerum līberant?

# Seek and Find!

1. Find eleven adjectives in the story and (circle) them. Include the number words. Include **multās** (many). Include all repeats. Hint: Look in lines 4, 5, 6, 7, 9, and 10.
2. Find nine *singular* verbs in the story and <u>underline</u> them. Include all repeats. Hints: Look in lines 1, <u>4, 5, 6</u>, 8, and 10. Remember the **-t** ending.
3. Find five *plural* nouns in the story and put parentheses ( ) around them. Include **grātiās** (thanks). Include all repeats. Hint: Look in lines 4, 7, 9, and 10.

# Partners

(Circle) the form of the adjective that makes a partnership with the noun. Remember to check the gender (*m, f, n*) and number (singular, plural) of the noun. Then translate any *two* of the sentences.

1. Mopsus est (bonus, bona, bonum).
2. Ātrium est (pulcher, pulchra, pulchrum).
3. Amābilis est (laetus, laeta, laetum).
4. Fenestrae sunt (longa, longus, longae).
5. Puer est (malus, mala, malum).

dominate

inhabit

insulate

magnify

domesticate

liberate

ridicule

prolong

### Chariot Race

Help the Roman Pacers win the chariot race. Complete each of the sentences below with a word from the list. Use the clues in parentheses ( ).

1. Claudius decided to (set free) _____ his slave Quintus.

2. Flavia's older brother Tiberius always tried to (control) _____ her.

3. The members of the household (live in) _____ a house.

4. We put on heavy coats to (protect) _____ ourselves against the cold.

5. A microscope is used to (make larger) _____ an object.

6. Felix tried to (housebreak) _____ his dog.

7. Lucius wanted to (laugh at) _____ Publius when he ran out of the cold water.

8. Do you want to (make longer) _____ the school year?

Check your answers with your teacher. Put a circle around every word in the list that you used correctly. Did you circle all the words and help the Pacers reach the goal?

# FIRST LATIN
## A Language Discovery Program

## BOOK II
### Daily Life

Marion Polsky

Longman

# FIRST LATIN

## A Language Discovery Program

### BOOK II

#### Daily Life

# Student Activity Book II

# Contents

# WELCOME BACK TO ROME!

By now you have learned a lot about the ancient Romans—the stories of their gods and heroes, the size of their Empire, the famous monuments in their largest city, **Rōma**, the styles of their houses and apartments, and the make-up of the Roman **familia**.

You also have learned about the language of the Romans, Latin. You know what it looks like and how it sounds. You can speak some Latin with your classmates.

You have seen firsthand that Latin is the key to English vocabulary. You know, for example, that *union, unite,* and *unique* have to do with the meaning "one" because you know the Latin word for *one,* **ūnus**!

The best is yet to come. In this book you will find out what the Romans wore, what they ate for dinner, how they entertained themselves at home and in the city, what a Roman school was like, how people earned a living, and much more. You will even attend a Roman wedding ceremony.

As you go along, your understanding of Latin will grow. You will be able to write your own Latin sentences and to see how sentences in Latin and in English are put together. Of course, your English vocabulary will become much larger, too.

As our story continues, Claudius, Antonia, and the rest of the family are at home. It is morning. . . .

4

# Part
# THREE
# *The Familia at Home*

In this unit, you will:

visit the family of Claudius at home
find out what Romans wore every day
describe the foods you eat in Latin
look inside the kitchen of Mopsus
read a story about a Roman dinner party
learn the Latin words for colors
sing a Latin song about eating and drinking
discover how English words are put together
learn many English words that come from Latin

5

# Māne

## In Cubiculō

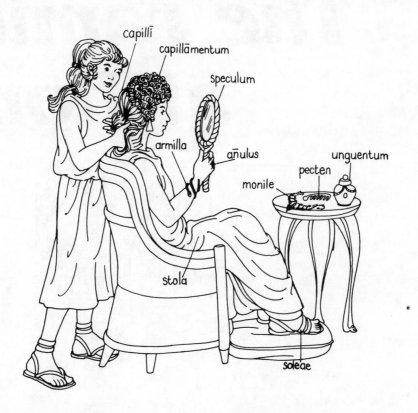

Antonia spent most of her morning getting dressed, with Amabilis' help.
Look at the ten Latin words in the picture above. As you read the story, fill
in the Latin names of the items Antonia uses to make herself beautiful.

AMABILIS: **Salvē, domina**! I see you've already put on your yellow

_____ with the blue border. May I put

_____ on your feet?

ANTONIA: **Ita vērō, Amābilis**. And hurry up. I'm meeting Julia
Aemilia, the senator's wife, for lunch! Comb my

_____ with the ivory

_____. Be sure to add the curly

_____ on top to make my hair look
higher.

6

AMABILIS: **Bene, domina**. Now I'll put on your makeup—white powder, red lip color, cheek rouge, and that new bright blue eye shadow.

ANTONIA: Don't forget my _____. I want to smell like a rose. And I'll wear a little jewelry—a gold

_____ or two on each finger, the

emerald _____ around my neck, the

gold and pearl _____ on one arm, and the lacy gold one on the other.

AMABILIS: There! You look lovely, **domina**.

ANTONIA: (*looking at herself in the* _____): Oh no!

AMABILIS: (*frightened*): What is it, **domina**?

ANTONIA: **Stulta serva es, Amābilis**! You forgot to pluck my eyebrows!

## Language Discovery: Ita aut Minimē?

Answer the following questions in Latin. Use the examples to help you.

1. Estne Antōnia māter?

   *Ita. Antonia māter est.*

2. Estne Quīntus dominus?

   *Minimē. Quīntus nōn est dominus. Libertus est.*

3. Estne Claudia puella Rōmāna?

   _____

4. Estne Rēx fēlēs?

   _____

5. Suntne Mopsus et Amābilis dominī?

   _____

6. Estne Bella parva?

   _____

7. Suntne stolae longae?

   _____

TURN THE PAGE FOR MORE

7

8. Suntne Graecia et Hispānia in Eurōpā?

_____

9. (answer if you're a **puella**) Esne discipula Americāna?
   (answer if you're a **puer**) Esne discipulus Rōmānus?

_____

# Colōrēs

Here are words for colors in Latin. They are adjectives.

|  | **m** | **f** | **n** |
|---|---|---|---|
| _white_ | alb**us**, | alb**a**, | alb**um** |
| _black_ | niger, | nigra, | nigrum |
| _yellow_ | flāvus, | flāva, | flāvum |
| _green_ | virid**is**, | virid**is**, | virid**e** |
| _red_ | rubidus, | rubida, | rubidum |
| _blue_ | caeruleus, | caerulea, | caeruleum |
| _purple_ | purpureus, | purpurea, | purpureum |
| _pink_ | roseus, | rosea, | roseum |

Match the item on the left below with a possible color word on the right. Remember that adjectives _agree_ with their nouns—the adjective ending changes, depending on whether the noun is masculine, feminine, or neuter. Each color word on the right is used only once.

1. __*C*__ crēta (_f_)                      a. viridis

2. _____ caelum (_n_ sky)                 b. rubidum

3. _____ herba (_f_ grass)                c. alba

4. _____ nimbus (_m_ cloud)              d. caeruleum

5. _____ flōs (_m_ flower)               e. caeruleum

6. _____ avis (_f_ bird)                 f. album

7. _____ fēlēs (_f_)                     g. nigra

8. _____ vexillum Americānum (_n_)       h. flāva

   _____                                 i. purpureus

   _____                                 j. roseus

9. _____ sōlis occāsus (_m_ sunset)      k. albus

**8**

# Poēma

Read aloud:

Rosae sunt rubidae
Violae sunt caeruleae
Saccharum est dulce
Etiam es tū!

## Vocabulary Help:

saccharum (n)—sugar
dulcis, dulcis, dulce—sweet
etiam—and so

# Fābella: Salūtātiō in Tablīnō

Persōnae: Claudius, Quīntus

Claudius sedet in tablīnō. Quīntus intrat.

| | | |
|---|---|---|
| QUĪNTUS: | Salvē, patrōne! Quid agis? | (1) |
| CLAUDIUS: | Et tū salvē, Quīnte! Bene valeō! Quid cupis hodiē? | (2) |
| QUĪNTUS: | Lībertus sum. Cupiō tabernam habēre et ānulōs | (3) |
| | facere. Cupiō esse ānulārius. | (4) |
| CLAUDIUS: | Bene. Cupisne pecūniam? | (5) |
| QUĪNTUS: | Ita vērō! Gemmās rubidās, viridēs, caeruleās, roseās, | (6) |
| | purpureās, flāvās, et nigrās emere cupiō. | (7) |
| CLAUDIUS: | Amīcus es, Quīnte! Pecūniam tibi libenter dabō. | (8) |
| QUĪNTUS: | Multās grātiās, patrōne, tibi agō. | (9) |
| CLAUDIUS: | Bonam fortūnam! Valē, Quīnte! | (10) |
| QUĪNTUS: | Valē, patrōne optime! | (11) |

## Vocabulary Help:

(Introduction) intrat—enters
(1) Quid agis?—How are you?
(2) Bene valeō!—I'm well!
  Quid cupis?—What do you want?
  hodiē—today
(3) cupiō—I want
  tabernam habēre—to have a shop
  ānulōs facere—to make rings
(4) esse—to be
  ānulārius—ring-maker

(5) Cupisne?—Do you want?
  pecūniam—money
(6) Ita vērō!—Yes, indeed!
  gemmās—gemstones, jewels
(7) emere cupiō—I want to buy
(8) tibi—to you
  libenter—gladly
  dabō—I'll give
(10) Bonam fortūnam!—Good luck!

9

# LECTIŌ XIII

# Domī

## Language Discovery

Here are sentences you have heard in class. Write the translation of each in the space provided.

1. Claudius sedet. _____

2. Antōnia sedet. _____

3. Antōnia et Claudius sedent. _____

Circle the ending on the verb in sentence 1 that makes it singular.
Circle the ending on the verb in sentence 3 that makes it plural.

These are some other verbs you have seen or heard:

| | | | | |
|---|---|---|---|---|
| habitat | agit | est | habitant | dormiunt |
| dormit | sunt | agunt | lūdit | lūdunt |

Put them in the chart below, in the correct column:

| Singular | Plural |
|---|---|
| *sedet* | *sedent* |
| _____ | _____ |
| _____ | _____ |
| _____ | _____ |
| _____ | _____ |

Fill in the blanks from the choices at the right to complete each sentence.

1. Claudius in tablīnō _____. (sedet, sedent)

2. Quīntus et Lūcius _____ in ātriō. (est, sunt)

3. Mopsus in culīnā _____. (cantat, cantant)

4. Servī in triclīniō _____. (stat, stant)

5. Rēx in peristȳliō _____. (ambulat, ambulant)

Read the completed Latin sentences silently. Can you translate each one?

10

Here are Latin root-forms for some of the verbs you have studied:

| stat | sedet | agit | dormit |
|------|-------|------|--------|
| "stand" | "sit" | "do, move" | "sleep" |
| stā- | sed- | ag- | dorm- |
| stat- | sess- | āct- | |
| statu- | | | |

Match each English word in the column at the left with its meaning in the column at the right. As you go along, use the *basic meaning* of each **Latin root-form** as a clue.

1. _____ **sta**ble      A. a building with rooms for *sleeping*

2. _____ **sed**entary      B. a building for horses and cows to *stand* in

3. _____ **ag**ent      C. something that has been *done*

4. _____ **dorm**itory      D. *sitting* down

5. _____ **stat**ic      E. in a *sleeping* state

6. _____ **act**      F. to *move* violently, stir up

7. _____ **dorm**ant      G. a *standing* figure carved of stone or made of clay

8. _____ **statu**e      H. a person who *does* something (for someone else)

9. _____ **ag**itate      I. a meeting in which everybody *sits* down

10. _____ **sess**ion      J. *standing* or remaining still

Write down two more English words you know from the root-form **āct-**:

_____      _____

Write down two more English words you know from **stā-**, **stat-**, or **statu-**:

_____      _____

### ???????A Word Mystery???????

Why is a *navigator* like a sailor?

Clues: 1. **nāvis** means "a ship"    2. **ig**- means "move" (from **ag**-)
       3. **-ate** means "(to) make"    4. **-or** means "someone who"

Solution: He's 4._____    3._____    1._____    2._____

**11**

## Making New Words

One way to make more words from the same Latin root-form is to add word starters or *prefixes* to the root. Each Latin prefix has a special meaning. Play the *If* Game to see how the meaning of the prefix and the meaning of the root-form are put together:

1. **pre-** "before, in front of"
   (Latin **prae-**, as in **praenōmen**, "before the **nōmen**")

   If **sid-** (from **sed-**) means "sit," what does a *president* do?

   Answer: He ___*sits in front of*___ everyone else.

   If **fix-** means "placed," what part of a word is the *prefix*?

   Answer: It's the part placed _____ the word.

   **Pre-** appears with many English words, such as *prehistoric*, *premature*, and *preview*. Use a dictionary to find more **pre-** words in English. Check to see if the root-word after the prefix comes from Latin or another language.

2. **re-** "back, again"

   If **port-** means "carry," what does a *reporter* do?

   Answer: She _____ a message.

   If **viv-** means "live," what happens when you *revive* someone who has

   fainted? Answer: The person _____.

   **Re-** is one of the most common prefixes in English: *reheat*, *reappoint*, *react*, *refuel*, *reflector*. Use a dictionary to find more **re-** words.

3. **trans-** "across"

   If **port-** means "carry," what do you do when you *transport* furniture?

   Answer: You _____.

   If **mit-** means "send," what happens when you *transmit* a message?

   Answer: You _____ the message to another person.

   Find the meanings of *transfix*, *transfusion*, *transit*.

12

**Ubi Est Claudia?**

CLAUDIA EST <u>I</u> __ __ __ __ __ __ __ __ __ __ __.
  1  2    3  4  5  6  7    8  9  10  11  12

Circle the word that is most nearly the *opposite* in meaning to the capitalized word. Use the meaning of the Latin root-form to help you. When you have finished, place the letter that is next to each circled word in the appropriate blank space above. The first one has been done for you.

1. STATIONARY
   (H) standing still
   (I) (moving)
   (J) fixed

2. NAVIGATOR
   (N) farmer
   (O) sailor
   (P) pilot

3. SEDATE
   (A) energetic
   (B) calm
   (C) peaceful

4. DORMITORY
   (R) bedrooms
   (S) dorm
   (T) gymnasium

5. STABLE
   (Q) steady
   (R) shaky
   (S) standing

6. SEDENTARY
   (I) walking
   (L) sitting
   (M) unmoveable

7. ACTOR
   (N) performer
   (O) spectator
   (P) mover

8. SESSION
   (I) a sitting together
   (L) meeting
   (M) journey

9. AGITATE
   (A) calm down
   (B) move violently
   (C) stir up

10. AMBULATORY
    (E) in motion
    (F) walking
    (G) lying down

11. DORMANT
    (N) wide awake
    (O) asleep
    (P) resting

12. PRESIDE
    (N) sit in front of
    (O) take orders
    (P) be in charge

# In Culīnā

## Cibī Rōmānī

As you read about Roman foods, think of the foods you usually eat. Which ones are the same? Which are different? Would you enjoy eating at the house of Lucius and Claudia?

### What Were the Most Important Roman Foods?

The soil and sunlight of Italy were a blessing for Roman farmers of ancient times, as well as today. Bountiful fruit (**pōma**) and vegetables (**holera**), along with salt-water fish (**piscēs**) from the surrounding seas, provided our Roman with a healthy, vitamin-rich diet. The three main food staples for all Romans came from the soil: grapes (**ūvae**) for wine (**vīnum**), olives (**olīvae**) for cooking oil and flavoring, and wheat (**trīticum**) for cooked cereal and bread.

### What Kinds of Meat (Carnēs) and Birds (Avēs) Did They Have?

For the ordinary Roman, meat was a rare treat. Beef (**būbula**) was enjoyed only on very special occasions, such as religious festivals in which a cow was sacrificed to the gods. Pork (**porcīna**) and lamb (**agnīna**) were a little more common, but only for people who could pay for them. A poor man might eat goat's meat (**caprīna**) once in a while. A chicken (**pullus**), goose (**anser**), duck (**anas**), or pigeon (**columba**) would be part of the dinner of a wealthy family.

14

## What Kinds of Fish (Piscēs) Did They Eat?

Fish was a basic part of the Roman diet. Many kinds of salt fish were eaten, and fishing was an important industry. One favorite dish of rich and poor alike was a hash made of fish, eggs (**ōva**), and cheese (**cāseus**). But our Quintus would not be able to afford fish every day. Very rich men had ponds at their country houses (**vīllae**). This way they could have fresh-water fish as well. Oysters (**ostreae**) were a popular appetizer among the rich.

## Did They Drink Milk (Lac)?

Yes, they did, but much less of it than children today. The favorite drink for Romans of all ages was wine (**vīnum**), mixed with water (**aqua**) or honey (**mel**). The most important dairy product in the Roman diet was cheese (**cāseus**), made from the milk of cows, goats, and sheep. It was even used as a spread on bread. Butter was *never* eaten; it was used as an ointment for burns and cuts.

## What Kinds of Bread (Pānis) Did They Have?

Wheat (**trīticum**) was the grain eaten in ancient Rome. In fact, the main dinner dish for most Romans was porridge (**puls**), a cooked cereal made from crushed wheat boiled with water. Bread—white, whole wheat, or wheat bran—was usually purchased at a bakery, where the flour was also ground. Loaves were round and had grooves for cutting individual slices. White bread was a luxury. Dark bread was usual in most Roman homes.

## What Were Common Fruits (Pōma) and Vegetables (Holera)?

The choice was very large, since even foreign varieties were brought to Italy to flourish in the rich soil. Asparagus (**asparagus**), beets (**bētae**), beans (**fabae**), mushrooms (**fungī**), lettuce (**lactūca**), and radishes (**rādicēs**) were all popular. Salad was a usual dinner course. Fruits included the fig (**fīcus**), strawberry (**frāgum**), apple (**mālum**), pear (**pirum**), plum (**prūnum**), and, of course, grapes (**ūvae**) of all types. These nutritious foods were eaten by rich and poor alike.

## Did They Drink Coffee?

Lucius wouldn't have a word for it! In fact, certain foods that are staples in the modern American kitchen were unknown in ancient Rome: oranges, corn, potatoes, tomatoes, coffee, and tea. Sugar (**saccharum**) was known but not used, because honey (**mel**) was preferred.

### Then and Now: Food and Drink

List the top ten foods and beverages you have most of the time. Be honest! Make a similar list for the ancient Romans, based on the reading. Compare the two lists. What items are the same?

# Word Search: Cibī Rōmānī

Find and circle the Latin words for the food items pictured. Words may go across, down, or on the diagonal, but they are never backward.

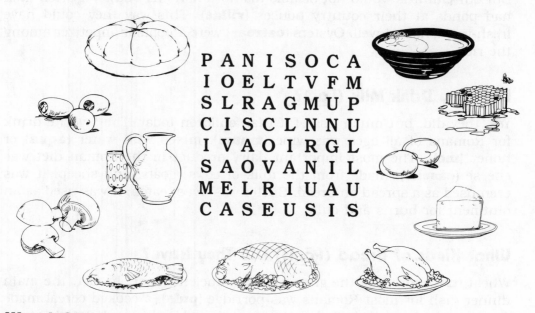

```
P A N I S O C A
I O E L T V F M
S L R A G M U P
C I S C L N N U
I V A O I R G L
S A O V A N I L
M E L R I U A U
C A S E U S I S
```

# Word Play

I. **Pānis, pān-** (bread) is the root of several English words:

**pan**try, "a room or closet to store food (bread)"
com**pan**ion, "a friend (a person you would share bread with)"
com**pan**y, "invited guests"
accom**pan**y, "to go as a companion with someone else"

Fill in the blanks with a word from the **pan-** list:

1. Claudius often invites _____ to dinner.

2. Lucius decided to _____ Claudius to the shop.

3. Lucius was the _____ of Claudius.

4. Dry food may be stored in a _____.

II. Fill in the word chain with these words from **vīnum, vīn-** (wine):

       *vine*         *vinegar*         *vineyard*

Wine is made from grapes that grow on a _____

in a _____. When wine turns sour, it is

called _____.

## Mopsus et Rēx

| | |
|---|---|
| Rēx in culīnā dormit. Mopsus vīnum portat. | (1) |
| Mopsus canem nōn videt. Cadit. | (2) |
| Nunc vīnum est in tunicā Mopsī. | (3) |
| "Male canis! Male canis!" inquit servus. | (4) |
| "Bau, bau! Bau, bau!" lātrat canis. | (5) |
| Rēx, oculīs magnīs, Mopsum spectat. | (6) |
| Mopsus Rēgem spectat et rīdet. | (7) |
| Duo iterum sunt amīcī bonī. | (8) |

---

### Vocabulary Help:

(1) portat—is carrying

(2) nōn videt—doesn't see
    cadit—he falls down

(3) nunc—now
    in tunicā Mopsī—on
        Mopsus' tunic

(4) male—bad

inquit—says

(5) Bau, bau!—Woof, woof!
    lātrat—barks

(6) oculīs magnīs—with his big eyes
    spectat—looks at

(7) rīdet—(he) laughs

(8) iterum—again

---

### Respondē Latīnē:

1. Quid portat Mopsus?
2. Quid est in tunicā Mopsī?
3. Quid inquit Mopsus?
4. Quid agit Rēx?

17

# Mini-Review III

## Circle It!

Circle the form of the verb that correctly completes each sentence.

1. Claudius in sellā (sedet, sedent).
2. Claudius et Lūcius in urbe (habitat, habitant).
3. Serva in cubiculō (dormit, dormiunt).
4. Rēx in peristȳliō (est, sunt).
5. Discipulī in camerā (cantat, cantant).

Circle the form of the adjective that correctly completes each sentence.

1. Aqua est (bonus, bona, bonum).
2. Fungī sunt (longus, longī, longae).
3. Suntne olīvae (rotunda, rotundī, rotundae)?
4. Estne piscis (bonus, bona, bonum)?
5. Estne vīnum (malus, mala, malum)?

## True or False?

Mark each statement below TRUE or FALSE.

1. _____ Roman clothing styles were the same for hundreds of years.

2. _____ The ritual called the **salūtātiō** took place in the evening.

3. _____ Roman women sometimes wore wigs.

4. _____ Children wore the **bulla** to protect them from evil spirits.

5. _____ The basic article of clothing for Roman women was the **toga**.

6. _____ Roman clothing was usually made of cotton.

7. _____ The three most important foods grown on Roman soil were wheat, olives, and grapes.

8. _____ The Romans usually sweetened their foods with sugar.

9. _____ In Roman times, white bread was more common than dark bread.

10. _____ Poor people often ate a wheat porridge for dinner.

All the English words in this tree come from *one* verb: **stāre**, which means "to stand." This verb has *seven* root-forms, each forming a branch of the tree:

**stā-**   **stat-**   **stin-**   **sist-**   **statu-**   **statut-**   **stitut-**

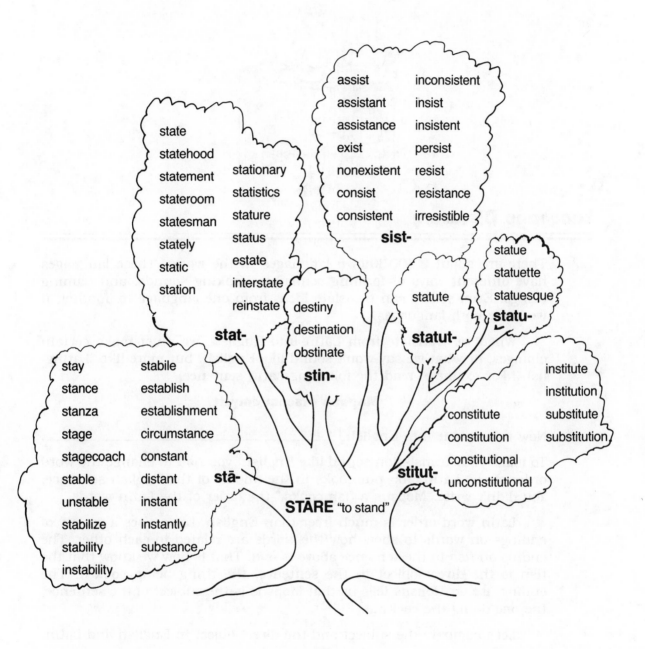

In the tree above:
1. Underline the Latin root-form in each English word.
2. Circle *five* words that you already know.
3. Choose *seven* words that you don't know—one for each root-form. Look them up in a dictionary.

# LECTIŌ XV

# Edāmus et Bibāmus!

## Language Discovery

There are about 3,500 known languages in the world. These languages have different ways of forming sentences, making sounds, and naming things. Even so, we can translate ideas from one language to another, if we know both languages.

When we translate from Latin into English, we must make certain changes, or what we say won't sound like English, but more like "Latinglish"! For example, read the following Latin sentence:

### Mopsus piscem coquit.

Now translate it into English. _____.

To make your translation sound like English, you had to change the word order of the Latin. You put *cooks* in the middle of the English sentence. You didn't write "Mopsus a fish cooks," the order of the Latin words.

Latin word order is much freer than English. Latin uses a variety of endings on words to show how the words are related to each other. The ending on *fish* in the sentence above is **-em**. That is how we know that the fish is the direct object in the sentence, the thing being cooked. The ending **-us** on *Mopsus* tells us that Mopsus is the subject of the sentence, the one doing the cooking.

Let's compare the subject and the direct object in English and Latin.

| Latin | English |
|---|---|
| Stola est longa. | The stola is long. |
| Antōnia stolam gerit. | Antonia is wearing the stola. |

Underline the forms of **stola** in both the Latin and English sentences above.

20

How many forms does **stola** have in the two Latin sentences? _____

Write them here: _____ _____

How many forms does *stola* have in the two English sentences? _____

Write it here: _____

Write the Latin sentence in which **stola** is the *direct object*. Write the English translation underneath.

_____

_____

Circle the direct object in each sentence.
What is the clue on the ending of the Latin word that tells you **stolam** is

the direct object? _____ Does the English *stola* have this clue?

_____ English uses *word order* to signal the direct object. In English, the direct object comes at the end of the sentence, after the verb. Underline the verb *is wearing* in the English sentence. Notice that *stola* comes after it.

Latin uses *endings*, not word order, as its main signal. So in Latin you can change the word order and still keep the meaning of the sentence. **Stolam** will always be the direct object because it ends in *-am* and **Antōnia** will always be the subject because it ends in *-a* (like **puella**):

| | |
|---|---|
| Antōni**a** gerit stol**am**. | *or* |
| Antōni**a** stol**am** gerit. | *or* |
| Gerit Antōni**a** stol**am**. | *or* |
| Gerit stol**am** Antōni**a**. | *or* |
| Stol**am** gerit Antōni**a**. | |

All of these versions of the sentence have the same basic meaning:

Antonia is wearing the stola.

But look what happens if we mix up the word order in English:

Antonia the stola is wearing.
Is wearing Antonia the stola.
Is wearing the stola Antonia.
The stola is wearing Antonia.

The first three versions are not English sentences. The last version doesn't make much sense, and its meaning is completely different from the original version. In English, if we change the word order, we change the meaning of the entire sentence.

**21**

I. Complete these sentences with the appropriate words or phrases:

1. In English, the order of _____ in a sentence signals which word is the subject and which word is the _____ _____. The direct object comes after the _____ or action word. The subject in an English sentence usually comes _____ in the sentence.

2. In Latin, the _____ on a noun signals whether it is the subject or the _____ _____ of the sentence. The very last letter of a direct object in Latin is usually _____. The subject of a sentence also has endings. For words like **Mopsus** and **servus**, the ending of the subject is _____. For words like **Antōnia** and **serva**, the ending of the subject is _____. The order of _____ in a Latin sentence may be changed without changing the basic meaning of the sentence.

II. Choose the noun with the appropriate ending and fill in the blank. Then translate each sentence.

1. Mopsus _____ coquit. (pānis, pānem)

_____

2. _____ aquam bibit. (Rēx, Rēgem)

_____

3. Togam gerit _____. (Claudius, Claudium)

_____

4. _____ edunt Lūcius et Claudia. (piscis, piscem)

_____

5. Rēx _____ amat (likes). (Bella, Bellam)

_____

# Word Play

I. Name it! The words in italics are derived from Latin root-forms you have learned:

**ed-** "eat"  **bib-** "drink"  **pān-** "bread"  **aqu-** "water"  **vīn-** "wine"

1. Name something *edible*. _____

2. Name something *inedible*. _____

3. Name an *aquatic* activity or sport. _____

4. Name something you can *imbibe*. _____

5. Name the main food that was stored in a *pantry*. _____

6. Name an animal you find in an *aquarium*. _____

7. Name something that is *aquamarine* in color. _____

8. Name a fruit that grows on a *vine*. _____

9. Name the place you need an *Aqua-Lung*. _____

10. Coffee is an *aqueous* liquid. Name another._____

II. Write a humerous short story using the following words:

    *pantry    company    vinegar    aquarium    imbibe*

_____

_____

_____

_____

_____

_____

_____

_____

_____

# In Triclīniō

## Lūcius Edit

Complete the following sentences by selecting the correct form of the word in parentheses. Use the picture clue to help you.

1. Lūcius edit _pānem_. (pānis, pānem, pānēs)

2. Claudius edit _____. (olīvae, olīvam, olīvās)

3. Bella edit _____. (piscis, piscem, piscēs)

4. Quīntus edit _____. (cāseus, cāseum, cāseōs)

5. Rēx bibit _____. (aqua, aquam, aquās)

6. Amabilis gerit _____. (solea, soleae, soleās)

7. Mopsus gerit _____. (tunica, tunicam, tunicās)

8. Claudia et Lūcius gerunt _____. (bulla, bullam, bullās)

9. Antōnia edit _____. (fungus, fungum, fungōs)

10. Mopsus coquit _____. (pullus, pullum, pullōs)

11. Antōnia habet _____. (ānulus, ānulum, ānulōs)

12. Mopsus spectat _____. (Rēx, Rēgem, Rēgēs)

24

On the next page you will read a story about a dinner party at the house of Claudius and Antonia. Elegant dinner parties were very popular among wealthy Romans. There were no movie theaters, evening concerts, or nightclubs in ancient Rome, and, of course, no television. So parties with friends were the only evening entertainment.

When guests arrived, Claudius would greet them. Male guests would remove their togas and sandals. Sometimes a man put on a light-colored robe (**synthesis**) over his tunic. Each guest also brought his own cloth napkin and a personal slave to wash his hands and look after him. At the end of the party, guests often took home some special food goodies wrapped in their napkins, like "doggy bags" at restaurants today!

Romans dined in a reclining position on couches set around a table in the **triclīnium**. There were usually three couches, with up to three guests at each. For *very* large parties, there were several sets of couches and tables. Roman ate with their fingers from dishes carried to the table by slaves. They washed their hands between courses, sometimes with rose water. Flowers and perfumes were often used to sweeten the air.

After dinner, or while having dessert, guests might be entertained by dancers, jugglers, and poets. Lots of gossip was also exchanged. Romans always loved a good story.

Extremely rich people gave huge banquets that have been described in detail by Roman authors. We know for a fact that there were dozens of courses and that the eating and drinking went on for hours, even days. Some of the dishes served were extremely rare and expensive so that the host could show off. Imagine, for example, a dish of fish livers, flamingo tongues, and peacock brains blended together!

Such luxury was not usual, of course. For the **cēna magna** of our Claudius, there would be three or four appetizers, two or three main dishes, and a choice of desserts, all accompanied by plenty of wine.

Now turn the page. **Legāmus!**

## Cēna Magna

Servī cēnam magnam parant. Mopsus fungōs, ōva, piscēs, (1)
pullōs, et cētera coquit. Amābilis vīnum rubidum et olīvās nigrās (2)
in triclīnium portat. (3)

Antōnia est laeta. Novam stolam flāvam gerit. Claudius (4)
est laetus. Synthesem purpureum gerit. Convīvae Antōniam et (5)
Claudium salūtant. Antōnia et Claudius convīvās quoque salūtant. (6)
Omnēs in triclīniō cēnant. (7)

---

### Vocabulary Help:

(1) parant—prepare
(2) et cētera—and the rest [of the dinner]
(3) in triclīnium—into the dining room
(4) laeta—happy
novam—new

flāvam—yellow
(5) synthesem—dining-robe
convīvae—the guests
(6) salūtant—greet
quoque—also
(7) omnēs—everybody, all
cēnant—dine, eat dinner

Amīcī vīnum amant et bibunt. Antōnia fungōs amat. Antōnia (8)
multōs fungōs edit. Mox aegerrima est. Faciēs viridis est. (9)

Subitō Antōnia surgit et ē triclīniō exit. Deinde Claudius exit. (10)
Tandem omnēs convīvae exeunt. Tōta cēna in mēnsā manet. (11)
Cēna magna perditur! (12)

---

### Vocabulary Help:

(8) amīcī—the friends
amant—like, love
(9) multōs—many
mox—soon
aegerrima—very sick
faciēs—(her) face
(10) subitō—suddenly
surgit—gets up

ē triclīniō—from the
dining-room
exit—goes out
deinde—then
(11) tandem—finally
tōta cēna—the whole dinner
manet—remains
(12) perditur—is ruined

---

### Respondē Latīnē:
1. Quid agit Mopsus?
2. Quid portat Amābilis?
3. Cūr (Why) est Antōnia laeta?
4. Quid agunt convīvae?
5. Ubi cēnant omnēs?

6. Quid amant amīcī?
7. Quae edit Antōnia?
8. Estne faciēs Antōniae viridis?
9. Quid subitō agit Antōnia?
10. Ubi manet tōta cēna?

# Language Discovery

Look at line 1 in the story: **Servī cēnam magnam parant**.

Translate the sentence: _____

What is the subject of this sentence? _____

What is the direct object? _____  _____

What is the verb or action word? _____

Look at lines 8-9 in the story: **Antōnia multōs fungōs edit**.

Translate the sentence: _____

What is the subject of this sentence? _____

What is the direct object? _____  _____

What is the verb or action word? _____

Find and underline *four* other adjective-noun partners that are direct objects. The nouns are **vīnum** (line 2), **olivās** (2), **stolam** (4), **synthesem** (5).

27

# Review III

## Vērum aut Falsum?

Put an X next to each sentence that is true. Then translate the *true* sentences in the spaces provided. The first one has been done for you.

1. __X__ Bella aquam bibit.

2. _____ Mopsus in tablīnō coquit.

3. _____ Claudia et Lūcius cum Bellā lūdunt.

4. _____ Mopsus togam gerit.

5. _____ Antōnia et Amābilis fungōs bibunt.

6. _____ Convīvae in triclīniō edunt.

7. _____ Vexillum Americānum est rubidum et album et caeruleum.

8. _____ Rosae sunt viridēs.

9. _____ Fēminae stolās longās gerunt.

10. _____ Rēx in īnsulā habitat.

11. _____ Cubiculum est magnum.

12. _____ Quīntus pecūniam et gemmās cupit.

1. _____ *Bella drinks water.* _____

_____

_____

_____

_____

28

# Seek and Find!

Underline the subjects and circle the direct objects in the English and Latin sentences below.

1. Mopsus wears a tunic.          Mopsus gerit tunicam.

2. Claudius wears a toga.         Claudius togam gerit.

3. Lucius sees Claudia.           Claudiam videt Lūcius.

4. The slave carries water.       Portat servus aquam.

5. Mopsus doesn't see Rex.        Mopsus Rēgem nōn videt.

# Cross It Out!

In each list, cross out *one* item that does not belong with the others.

1. Roman clothing: **stola, toga, tunica, soleae, fungus, palla, bulla**

2. Roman foods: **piscis, bētae, asparagus, stilus, cāseus, mel, pullus**

3. Colors: **purpureus, niger, parvus, flāvus, rubidus, caeruleus**

4. Sentence subjects: **servus, fēlēs, puella, Rēgem, Amābilis, parentēs**

5. Direct objects: **fungōs, olīvās, pānem, aqua, piscem, cēnam**

6. Plural verbs: **est, sunt, lūdunt, agunt, sedent, stant, vident**

7. Items in a **culīna**: pots, knives, oven, strainer, charcoal, toaster, spoons

8. Latin "people" words: **serva, ānulārius, domus, patrōnus, cliēns**

9. English words from **stāre**: stay, constant, sediment, statue, state

10. English words from **vīn-**: vine, vinegar, win, vineyard, wine

# Crossword Puzzle

Clue Words:

ĀNULĪ
BULLA
CĀSEUS
FUNGĪ
OLĪVAE
PĀNIS
PISCĒS
SOLEAE
TOGA
TUNICA

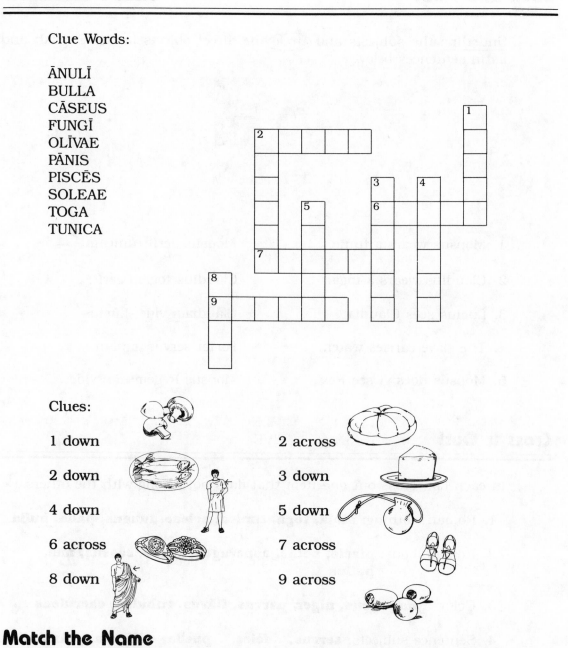

Clues:

1 down

2 down

4 down

6 across

8 down

2 across

3 down

5 down

7 across

9 across

# Match the Name

Place the number of the Latin word next to its description.

1. stola      _____ the main meal of the day in ancient Rome
2. cubiculum      _____ the good-luck pendant worn by Roman children
3. bulla      _____ the basic ankle-length dress of Roman women
4. toga      _____ the garment worn by Roman citizens (men only)
5. vīnum      _____ the room in which Amabilis groomed Antonia
6. salūtātiō      _____ the fruit from which cooking oil was extracted
7. tunica      _____ the room in which Mopsus fried fish
8. cēna      _____ the morning ritual between patron and client
9. culīna      _____ the favorite drink of Romans of all ages
10. olīva      _____ the basic knee-length clothing for men and boys

30

# Word Game

## Ubi Est Lūcius?

Find the correct English word to complete each sentence below. Put one letter in each blank. When you have finished, read down the circled letters to find out the answer.

Lūcius est in _____.

| | | | | |
|---|---|---|---|---|
| IMBIBE | PANTRY | EDIBLE | SEDATE | DORMANT |
| AQUEOUS | STABLE | ACTIVE | PISCES | PRESIDE |

1. The sign of the zodiac for people born between February 19 and

   March 20 is symbolized by two fish; it's called Ⓟ _ _ _ _ _.

2. A calm, settled person may be described as _ Ⓔ _ _ _ _.

3. The club president wanted to _ Ⓡ _ _ _ _ _ at all meetings.

4. When we are thirsty, we like to _ _ _ Ⓑ _ _ lots of water.

5. If you put a tea bag in water, you make an _ _ _ _ _ _ Ⓢ
   solution.

6. Mopsus was always busy doing tasks; he was _ _ Ⓣ _ _ _.

7. Bread and other foods are stored in a closet called a _ _ _ _ _ Ⓨ.

8. When horses are resting, they stand quietly in the _ _ _ _ Ⓛ _.

9. Were the mushrooms that Antonia ate _ _ Ⓘ _ _ _?

10. When a volcano like Mount Vesuvius in Italy does not erupt, it is

    said to be sleeping or _ Ⓞ _ _ _ _ _.

31

# Legāmus!

Read the story below. Then answer the questions in complete Latin sentences.

## Lūcius et Rēx

| | |
|---|---|
| Quīntus multōs ānulōs vēndit. In tabernā stat. | (1) |
| Subitō Rēgem videt. | (2) |
| "Ubi est Lūcius, Rēx?" rogat Quīntus. | (3) |
| "Bau, bau! Bau, bau!" lātrat Rēx. | (4) |
| Lūcius intrat. Īrātus est. | (5) |
| "Salvē, Quīnte!" clāmat. "Rēx, canis malus es! Venī hūc!" | (6) |
| Rēx ad Lūcium ambulat. Canis puerum spectat. | (7) |
| Lūcius rīdet. Lūcius Rēgem, amīcum bonum, amat. | (8) |
| Domī duo amīcī pānem rotundum edunt. Aquam bibunt. | (9) |
| Rēx in cubiculō Lūcī dormit. | (10) |

## Respondē Latīnē:

1. Vēnditne Quīntus ānulōs? _____

2. Ubi stat Quīntus? _____

3. Quem (Whom) videt? _____

4. Quis intrat tabernam? _____

5. Quid clāmat Lūcius? _____

6. Quid agit Rēx? (line 7) _____

7. Quid bibunt duo amīcī? _____

8. Ubi dormit Rēx? _____

# Part FOUR

# Activities in the City

In this unit, you will:

visit Quintus in his ring shop
discuss jobs and professions in ancient Rome
read a story about Lucius at school
spend an afternoon at the Roman Baths
learn the Latin words for parts of the body
sing a Latin song about everyday activities
attend Claudia's wedding
write your own Latin sentences
learn many English words that come from Latin

# Forum Rōmānum

## Legāmus!

Claudius, Antōnia, Lūcius, et Claudia per Forum Rōmānum ambulant.

Aemilius, Iūlia, Pūblius, et Līvia per Forum ambulant.

Lūcius Pūblium videt.
Lūcius: "Quō ambulās, Pūblī?"
Pūblius: "Ambulō ad lūdum, Lūcī! Venī!"
Duo puerī ad lūdum ambulant.

Claudius Aemilium videt.
Claudius: "Quō ambulās, Aemilī?"
Aemilius: "Ambulō ad Cūriam, Claudī! Venī!"
Duo senatōrēs ad Cūriam ambulant.

Antōnia et Claudia Iūliam et Līviam vident.
Iūlia: "Quō ambulātis, Antōnia et Claudia?"
Antōnia et Claudia: "Ambulāmus ad tabernam Quīntī. Venīte, Iūlia et Līvia!"
Duae fēminae et duae puellae ad tabernam Quīntī ambulant.

---

### Vocabulary Help:

per Forum Rōmānum—through the Roman Forum
Quō ambulās?—Where are you walking (to)?
Ambulō ad lūdum.—I'm walking to school.
ad Cūriam—to the Senate House
Quō ambulātis?—Where are you (two) walking (to)?
Ambulāmus ad tabernam Quīntī.—We are walking to Quintus' shop.

# Language Discovery

1. Complete this English verb chart for *walk*:

   I _____*walk*_____     we _____

   you (one person) _____     you (more than one person) _____

   he *or* she *or* it _____     they _____

   Circle the only form that has a special ending.

2. Here is the chart for *walk* in Latin:

   ambulō ____*I walk*____     ambulāmus _____

   ambulās _____     ambulātis _____

   ambulat _____     ambulant _____

   You have already learned the ending for *he, she,* or *it* in Latin. Circle the ending in the chart. Now circle the ending for *they*. Complete the English translation of the Latin forms.

3. English uses separate words—*I, you, he, she, it, we,* or *they*—to tell you who is doing the walking. Latin uses different endings on the verb instead. These are called *personal endings.*

   | Singular | | Plural | |
   |---|---|---|---|
   | **-ō** (or **-m**) | "I" | **-mus** | "we" |
   | **-s** | "you" | **-tis** | "you" |
   | **-t** | "he," "she," or "it" | **-nt** | "they" |

4. Here are some Latin verbs you know. Circle the personal endings. Then translate the Latin verb forms into English.

   sedeō _____     sedēmus _____

   sedēs _____     sedētis _____

   sedet ____*he sits*____     sedent _____

   bibō _____     bibimus _____

   bibis _____     bibitis _____

   bibit _____     bibunt _____

   portō _____     portāmus _____

   portās _____     portātis _____

   portat _____     portant _____

35

5. Complete this English verb chart:

| Singular | | Plural | |
|---|---|---|---|
| I | *am* | we | |
| you | *are* | you | |
| he | | they | |

Do you see that the singular forms are different from one another? That's because the verb *to be* is *irregular* in English. Compare the forms of *to walk*, which is regular.

6. Here is the chart for *to be* in Latin. It looks irregular, but notice that the personal endings are the same ones used in the other Latin verb charts. (The ending **-m** is sometimes used to mean "I" in Latin.)

| | | | |
|---|---|---|---|
| sum | *I am* | sumus | |
| es | | estis | |
| est | | sunt | |

Circle the personal endings. Then complete the English translation of the Latin verb forms.

7. How well do you know the Latin personal endings? Match the Latin verb in Column A with its translation in Column B.

| Column A | | Column B |
|---|---|---|
| 1. ambulō | _____ | A. she is |
| 2. est | _____ | B. they eat |
| 3. edunt | _____ | C. you (singular) walk |
| 4. sumus | _____ | D. I walk |
| 5. ambulās | _____ | E. I eat |
| 6. cantant | _____ | F. you (plural) are |
| 7. estis | _____ | G. they sing |
| 8. edō | _____ | H. we walk |
| 9. cantās | _____ | I. you (singular) sing |
| 10. ambulāmus | _____ | J. we are |

36

# Making New Words

If **ad lūdum** means "to school" and **ad tabernam** means "to the shop," what does **ad** mean by itself? _____

If **per Forum Rōmānum** means "through the Roman Forum," what does **per** mean by itself? _____

**Ad** (to) and **per** (through) also appear in English, as word starters or *prefixes*. You have studied other prefixes from Latin: **pre-, re-, trans-.**

Complete the English sentences below by adding the prefix **ad** or the prefix **per** in front of each word part. Hint: Look for a clue word, *to* or *through*, in each sentence.

1. A person ___*per*___spires *through* the pores of the skin.

2. Bandages _____here *to* the skin.

3. _____fumes send sweet orders *through* the air.

4. The nurse _____vanced *toward* the patient.

5. The baseball manager says he will _____mit the pitcher *to* the new team.

6. The stadium will last *throughout* the years because it is

   _____manent.

7. To go *into* a movie theater, you must pay the price of _____mission.

8. Flowers that bloom *through* the years are called _____ennials.


Now write down four of the words you have made with **ad** or **per**. Next to each word, put its meaning. Use a dictionary to help you.

| English Word | Meaning |
|---|---|
| _____ | _____ |
| _____ | _____ |
| _____ | _____ |
| _____ | _____ |

# LECTIŌ XVIII

# Taberna Quīntī

## Fābella: Quīntus Ānulārius

Persōnae: Quīntus, Antōnia, Claudia
Antōnia et Claudia tabernam Quīntī intrant. Multōs ānulōs vident. (1)

QUĪNTUS: Salvēte, fēminae! (2)
ANTŌNIA ET CLAUDIA: Salvē, Quīnte! (3)
QUĪNTUS: Cūr estis in Forō hodiē? Cupitisne ānulum? (4)
ANTŌNIA: Ita vērō! Fīlia mea ānulum cum gemmā cupit. (5)
    Nūptiae mox erunt. (6)
QUĪNTUS: Bene! Quālem ānulum cupis, Claudia? (7)
CLAUDIA: Ānulum magnum cum gemmā pulchrā cupiō. (8)
QUĪNTUS: Amāsne hunc ānulum cum sapphīrō? (9)
CLAUDIA: Minimē. Nōn est magnus. (10)
ANTŌNIA: Sed est pulcher! (11)
QUĪNTUS: Amāsne hunc ānulum cum onyche? (12)
CLAUDIA: Minimē. Nōn est pulcher. (13)
ANTŌNIA: Sed est magnus! (14)
QUĪNTUS: Amāsne hunc ānulum cum gemmā rubidā? (15)
CLAUDIA: Ita vērō! Hunc ānulum amō. Magnus et pulcher est. (16)
    Optimus est. Omnēs puellae hunc ānulum amābunt. (17)
ANTŌNIA: Claudius, pater tuus, quoque hunc ānulum amābit. (18)
    Ānulus nōn est cārus! (19)

---

### Vocabulary Help:

(4) Cupitisne?—Do you want?
(5) fīlia mea—my daughter
    cum gemmā—with a jewel, gem
(6) Nūptiae mox erunt.—Her
    wedding will take place
    soon.
(7) Quālem ānulum?—What sort of
    ring?
(9) hunc ānulum—this ring

sapphīrō—sapphire, a blue stone
(11) sed—but
(12) onyche—onyx, a black stone
(17) amābunt—will like
(18) pater tuus—your father
    quoque—also
    amābit—will like
(19) cārus—expensive

38

Ancient Romans did many different kinds of work, just as people do today. Here is a list of some Roman occupations. Read the descriptions below and place the name of the occupation in the appropriate blank.

farmer          barber          innkeeper          secretary          baker
undertaker      architect       doctor             florist            carriage driver

1. **Agricola sum.** I grow vegetables on my farm and sell them in the market in Rome. **Quis sum?** I am a _____.

2. **Tōnsor sum.** I cut hair and shave beards. I use a sharp razor. **Quis sum?** I am a _____.

3. **Medicus sum.** I take care of sick people with herbs and other drugs. I come from Greece. **Quis sum?** I am a _____.

4. **Caupō sum.** I rent out rooms in my inn to travelers. I have a restaurant on the ground floor. **Quis sum?** I am an

_____.

5. **Libitīnārius sum.** I prepare a dead body for a funeral. **Quis sum?**

I am an _____.

6. **Scrība sum.** I work in government service and perform many tasks, including writing letters and reports. **Quis sum?** I am a

_____.

7. **Rosārius sum.** I make garlands and bouquets of roses and sell them to customers. **Quis sum?** I am a _____.

8. **Architectus sum.** I design public buildings and temples to the gods. **Quis sum?** I am an _____.

9. **Pistor sum.** I bake bread in ovens in my shop and sell it fresh daily. **Quis sum?** I am a _____.

10. **Raedārius sum.** I drive a four-wheeled carriage which carries passengers on long journeys. **Quis sum?** I am a

_____.

Now try these:

lawyer        slave-dealer      dyer        shoemaker
painter       ring seller        merchant    poet
schoolteacher                                     sailor

1. **Litterātor sum.** I teach students until the age of fourteen. I teach reading, writing, and arithmetic. **Quis sum?** I am a

   _____.

2. **Pictor sum.** I am hired to paint and decorate the rooms in the houses of the rich. **Quis sum?** I am a _____.

3. **Sūtor sum.** I make leather shoes and sandals for men and women. **Quis sum?** I am a _____.

4. **Poēta sum.** I am paid to write poetry for special occasions—religious holidays, weddings, and military victories. **Quis sum?** I am a

   _____.

5. **Nauta sum.** I work on a ship that brings goods from foreign lands to Rome. The seaport is at Ostia, near Rome. **Quis sum?** I am a

   _____.

6. **Mercātor sum.** I buy all kinds of goods, like clothing, tools, and pots, and I sell them to small shopkeepers. **Quis sum?** I am a

   _____.

7. **Advocātus sum.** I go to court with my client and defend him. I get no legal fees, but I often accept gifts. **Quis sum?** I am a

   _____.

8. **Vēnālicius sum.** I sell slaves from many countries at the slave market in Rome. **Quis sum?** I am a _____.

9. **Tinctor sum.** I dye cloth for togas and stolas. I get my colors from plants and minerals. **Quis sum?** I am a _____.

10. **Ānulārius sum.** I make and sell rings in my shop. **Quis sum?** I am a _____. **Praenōmen mihi est Quīntus.**

**40**

I. Read aloud:

**Quīntus est ānulārius.  Quid agit Quīntus?  Quīntus ānulōs vēndit.**

Think of the meaning of **ānulārius**. What does **vēndit** mean? _____

Translate: **Quīntus ānulōs vēndit.** _____

Now fill in these sentences. They contain words from the root-form **vēnd-**.

1. The *vendor* at the ball game _____ hot dogs and ice cream.

2. A *vending machine* _____ you candy when you put a coin in it.

3. Quintus *vends* rings. He _____ them.

Which word is more familiar to you—*vends* or *sells*? Here's why:

Do you remember that the mother of the English language is Germanic? The word *sell* is a very old Germanic word in the English language. The word *vend* is a newer word in English. Like many Latin root-forms, when it came into English, *vend* did not replace the old word *sell*. But it gave us another way of saying the same thing. It made our vocabulary richer.

II. Fill in the blanks with the following words based on Roman occupations:

ARCHITECT   MEDICAL   TONSORIAL   ADVOCATE   MERCANTILE
SCRIBE      PICTORIAL  TINCTURE   POETRY     NAUTICAL

1. The person who designed the Colosseum was a great _____.

2. A sailor knows how to make _____ knots in a rope.

3. You will stain your clothes purple if you spill _____ of iodine.

4. The barber cut Publius' hair with _____ skill.

5. The doctor gave his _____ opinion about the sick patient.

6. Romans who couldn't write hired a _____ to help them.

7. Painted on the walls was a _____ history of ancient Rome.

8. Claudia's husband-to-be sent her a letter filled with love _____.

9. Merchants who sell goods may belong to a _____ union.

10. If, like a lawyer, you defend someone, you are his _____.

## Legāmus!

### Discipulus Malus

Puerī in lūdō sunt. Lūcius et Pūblius intrant. Magistrum salūtant. (1)
Amīcōs salūtant. Puerī sedent. Magister in sellā magnā sedet. (2)
Fābulam longam legit. Discipulī in cērīs fābulam scrībunt. (3)

Marcus, amīcus Lūcī et Pūblī, surgit. Lūcius et Pūblius (4)
susurrant, "Sedē, Marce!" Magister clāmat, "Sedē, Marce!" (5)
Marcus amīcōs nōn audit. Magistrum nōn audit. (6)

Magister surgit. Īrātus est. Ad Marcum ambulat et manum tollit. (7)
Marcus statim sedet. Omnēs discipulī tacent. (8)

### *Vocabulary Help:*

(1) in lūdō—in school
(3) fābulam—story
   legit—he is reading
   in cērīs—on wax tablets
   scrībunt—are writing
(4) surgit—gets up

(5) susurrant—whisper
(6) nōn audit—does not hear
(7) manum tollit—raises up his
   hand
(8) statim—immediately
   tacent—are silent

**Respondē Latīnē:**

1. Ubi sunt puerī?
2. Quid legit magister?
3. Quid agit Marcus?
4. Quī (Who) susurrant?

5. Quid clāmat magister?
6. Cūr surgit magister?
7. Quid tollit magister?
8. Quid agunt omnēs discipulī?

# Language Discovery: Building Blocks I

Letters are building blocks. You put letters together to make a word. Sentences are also put together from building blocks. Here are three sentence building blocks you have learned:

*The subject*—the person or thing that is doing something
*The verb*—the action word, like *write* or *read*
*The direct object*—the person or thing that receives the action

### Discipulī fābulam scrībunt.

Underline the subject once. Underline the direct object twice. Circle the

verb. Translate the sentence: _____.

Another building block you have seen many times is called a *prepositional phrase*. That's a long name for something you already know:

**in lūdō** "in school"                    **per Forum** "through the Forum"
**in cērīs** "on wax tablets"              **ad lūdum** "to school"
**in sellā magnā** "in a big chair"        **ad Marcum** "to Marcus"

See how the noun endings change, just as they do for the direct object? Don't worry about this. Just look for the word that comes in front of the noun, a word like **in**, **per**, and **ad**. These "little" words are called *prepositions*. They are always followed by a noun. Can you think of some Latin prepositional phrases you know by heart?

Try building your own Latin sentences. Use the building blocks below. Make up three sentences. Be sure your sentences make sense!

| Subjects | Direct Objects | Prepositional Phrases | Verbs |
|---|---|---|---|
| Puella | amīcam | in lūdō | coquit. |
| Puer | fābulam | in cērā | scrībit. |
| Mopsus | ānulum | in culīna | videt. |
| Magister | discipulum | in tabernā | audit. |
| Quīntus | piscem | in ātriō | vēndit. |

1. _____

2. _____

3. _____

**43**

If you *scribble* your name, is it *legible*? Probably not! *Scribble*, from **scrīb-**, means "to write in a careless or sloppy way." *Legible*, from **leg-**, means "able to be read, readable."

Here are the Latin root-forms for some new verbs in the reading story:

| **scrībit** | **legit** | **audit** |
|---|---|---|
| "write" | "read, choose" | "listen, hear" |
| **scrīb-** | **leg-** | **aud-** |
| **scrīpt-** | **lēct-** | **audit-** |

1. From the two **audit** root-forms, we get **aud**ience and **aud**itorium.
   If you speak loudly, you will be *audible*, "able to be heard."
   Two parts of your face that help your *auditory* sense are your

   _____.

2. By adding prefixes to **scrib-** and **script-**, we get the following pairs:

   | Verbs | Nouns |
   |---|---|
   | describe | description |
   | inscribe | inscription |
   | prescribe | prescription |

   Circle the prefixes. Which one is new? _____ It means "about."

   Which Latin root-form do the English *verbs* come from? _____

   Which Latin root-form do the English *nouns* come from? _____

   What is the ending, or *suffix*, on the nouns? _____

3. By adding prefixes to the root-form **lēct-**, we get these pairs:

   | Verbs | Nouns |
   |---|---|
   | collect | collection |
   | elect | election |
   | select | selection |

   Circle the prefixes: *col-* meaning "with, together," *e-* meaning "out of," and *se-* meaning "apart."

   What is the ending, or *suffix*, on the nouns? _____

4. List here up to six English words on this page you don't know. Underline the Latin root-forms. Then look up the words in a dictionary.

   _____  _____  _____

   _____  _____  _____

# Word Game

## *Listen! Read! Write!*

For each set, choose the word from the list at the top that best completes each sentence.

### AUD- and AUDĪT

AUDIENCE          AUDIBLE          AUDITORY          AUDIO

1. The ear doctor will test my _____ ability.

2. When the band finished playing, people in the _____ clapped.

3. I turned up the sound on the television to make it

   _____.

4. Alice's record player is part of her _____ system.

### LEG- and LĒCT

LEGIBLE          COLLECTION          ELECT          LECTURE

1. I have one hundred albums in my record _____.

2. Every four years, the people of the United States _____ a president.

3. The college professor had a large audience for his _____.

4. My teacher's handwriting is always _____.

### SCRĪB- and SCRĪPT-

SCRIBE          SCRIPT          DESCRIBE          INSCRIPTION

1. The written form of a language is known as _____.

2. A Roman who was hired to write letters and reports was a

   _____.

3. The movie monster was so horrible he was difficult to

   _____.

4. Claudia's wedding ring has an _____ inside the band.

45

# Mini-Review IV

## Quid Agit Lūcius?

Find the sentence that describes each picture and write it underneath.

Lūcius magistrum audit.
Lūcius in cērā scrībit.
Lūcius fābulam legit.

Lūcius in sellā sedet.
Lūcius susurrat.
Lūcius Pūblium salūtat.

## Find the Subject!

Circle the personal ending of each verb. Then translate the verb.

1. ambulās  _you walk_           4. audiunt _____

2. scrībō _____   5. editis _____

3. legimus _____  6. sum _____


## True or False?

Mark each statement below TRUE or FALSE. Read carefully!

1. _____ The city center of ancient Rome was the Forum.

2. _____ Women did not have occupations like men in ancient Rome.

3. _____ Most occupations in ancient Rome do not exist today.

4. _____ In Roman times books were written by hand.

5. _____ The school year for Lucius began in September.

6. _____ Students used an **abacus** to learn arithmetic.

7. _____ The training of young Roman girls was usually their mother's task.

8. _____ In an ancient Roman elementary school, the main subjects were reading, arithmetic, and science.


## Match the Word!

Match the English derivative with its meaning.

1. astronaut     _____ related to hearing
2. vendor        _____ care of the hands
3. legible       _____ star sailor
4. fable         _____ farming
5. auditory      _____ to choose
6. elect         _____ seller
7. manicure      _____ able to be read
8. agriculture   _____ a made-up story

**47**

## Language Discovery

1. Māne Claudia et Antōnia in Forō ambulābant.

2. Nunc Claudia et Antōnia ad thermās ambulant.

3. Māne Lūcius in lūdō sedēbat.

4. Nunc Lūcius in hortō sedet.

The activities on the left side of the page took place *in the morning*, **māne**. The activities on the right side of the page are happening *now*, **nunc**!

Look at the verb forms on the left. What letters do you see in front of the personal endings **-nt** and **-t**? Write them here. _____

When you see **-ba-** before the personal ending, you know that the action has already happened; it's over. We say that the action is in the *past*.

| | |
|---|---|
| Lūcius in cubiculō dormiē**ba**t. | Lucius **was** *sleeping* in the bedroom. |

The Latin verbs you learned *without the* **-ba-** show that the action is happening now, in the *present*.

| | |
|---|---|
| Lūcius in cubiculō *dormit*. | Lucius *is sleeping* in the bedroom. |

Notice that English also shows a difference between *present* and *past*:

| | |
|---|---|
| *is* sleeping | *was* sleeping |

Write the English translations of sentences 3 and 4 found on the opposite page. <u>Underline</u> the verb that shows action in the present. (Circle) the verb that shows action in the past.

3. _____

4. _____

Here are some present/past verb pairs in Latin. Look for the **-ba-**. Say each verb aloud. Then translate into English. The first one is done for you as an example.

1. ambulant *they walk*            ambulābant *they were walking*

2. lūdit _____          lūdēbat _____

3. audiunt _____        audiēbant _____

4. videt _____          vidēbat _____

5. amant _____          amābant _____

6. scrībit _____        scrībēbat _____

7. portant _____        portābant _____

8. clāmat _____         clāmābat _____

**49**

Most Romans didn't take showers or baths at home. In the hot afternoon, **post merīdiem**, all business stopped, stores were closed, and students put away their tablets. Everybody went to buildings all over the city called **thermae** (baths). The **thermae** were magnificent structures, decorated with marble, gold, and paintings. They were also gigantic. The Baths built by the Emperor Diocletian could hold more than 3,000 bathers at one time!

## Why Did Romans Like the Baths?

The **thermae** were not only for getting clean. They were equipped with gyms like a modern health club. There were gardens (**hortī**), swimming pools (**piscīnae**), restaurants, libraries, and open wrestling grounds, too. The **thermae** were centers of social activity in Rome, places to meet friends. Throughout the afternoon, people chatted, exercised, planned business deals, arranged dinner parties, played sports, and relaxed.

## How Did the Romans Bathe?

Men and women bathed in separate sections. Each section had at least four large enclosed rooms with different heat levels. First our Lucius would undress in a dressing room and store his clothes in a cubbyhole. Then he would enter the warm and steamy **tepidārium**. Next he would soak in a pool of hot water in the **caldārium**. Then he would enter the cold room or **frīgidārium** for a cold bath. The last stop was a rubdown and massage with olive oil by a trained slave. The oil would be removed by metal scrapers called **strigilēs**. Each bather brought his own oil, scrapers, and towels, carried by a personal slave.

## Are the Baths Still Used Today in Rome?

Because the public baths were so large, you can still see their brick remains today. The most famous are the Baths of the Emperor Caracalla, where operas are now held in the summer. Claudius and his family attended the Baths of the Emperor Trajan, near the Colosseum. These are now part of a public park. Other ancient baths are the sites of museums and churches. But none is now used for bathing.

### Then and Now: Roman Baths

Compare the Roman Bath with a modern health club or gym. Which features are similar? Which features are different? Be specific.

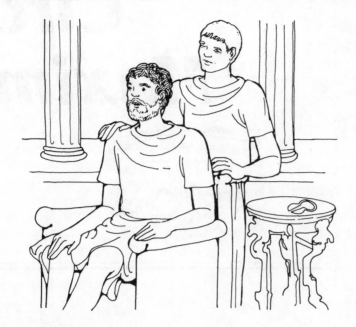

## Quīntus et Tōnsor

| | |
|---|---|
| Māne Quīntus in tabernā labōrābat. | (1) |
| Multōs ānulōs pulchrōs vēndēbat. Laetus erat. | (2) |
| Post merīdiem per Forum ambulābat. Tōnsōrem petēbat. | (3) |
| Tōnsor clāmābat, "Venī hūc! Barbās tondeō!" | (4) |
| Quīntus, "Barba mea est longa! Tondē barbam!" inquit. | (5) |
| Tōnsor rīdēbat. Novāculam petēbat. | (6) |
| Quīntus, "Novācula est in mēnsā!" inquit, "Cūr novāculam nōn vidēs?" | (7) |
| Iterum tōnsor rīdēbat. | (8) |
| "Oculī meī nōn sunt validī," inquit tōnsor, "sed manus est valida." | (9) |
| Quīntus timēbat. Quīntus nōn rīdēbat. | (10) |

---

### Vocabulary Help:

(2) laetus erat—he was happy

(3) tōnsōrem—a barber
    petēbat—he was looking for

(4) barbās—beards
    tondeō—I cut

(5) barba mea—my beard
    tondē!—cut!

inquit—said

(6) novāculam—his razor

(8) iterum—again

(9) oculī meī—my eyes
    validī—strong
    manus—(my) hand

(10) timēbat—was scared

---

### Respondē Latīnē:

1. Quid agēbat Quīntus māne?
2. Quandō (When) ambulābat Quīntus per Forum?
3. Quem (Whom) petēbat Quīntus in Forō?
4. Quid petēbat tōnsor?
5. Ubi erat (was) novācula?
6. Cūr nōn rīdēbat Quīntus?

# LECTIŌ XXI

# Circus Maximus

## Legāmus!

### Calamitās!

| | |
|---|---|
| Heri Lūcius ad lūdum nōn ambulābat. Diēs festus erat. | (1) |
| Puer cum patre et Pūbliō ad Circum Maximum ambulābat. | (2) |
| Equōs et aurīgās vidēre cupiēbat. | (3) |
| Puerī Rūfum spectābant. "Rūfus est aurīga optimus!" clāmābant. | (4) |
| Subitō omnēs spectātōrēs surrēxērunt. "Ecce! Ecce! | (5) |
| Rūfus cecidit! Ubi est medicus? Ubi est medicus?" clāmābant. | (6) |
| Medicus bonus aderat. Aurīgam cūrābat. | (7) |
| Rūfus oculōs lentē aperiēbat. "Aurīga valēbit," inquit medicus. | (8) |
| Spectātōrēs applaudēbant. Laetī erant. | (9) |

### Vocabulary Help:

Calamitās!—Accident!
(1) heri—yesterday
diēs festus erat—it was a
 holiday
(3) equōs—horses
aurīgās—charioteers
vidēre—to see
cupiēbat—he wanted
(4) aurīga—charioteer
(5) subitō—suddenly

surrēxērunt—got up
Ecce!—Look!
(6) cecidit—has fallen down
(7) aderat—was present
cūrābat—he was taking care of
(8) lentē—slowly
aperiēbat—opened
valēbit—will be all right
(9) applaudēbant—were applauding
erant—they were

### Respondē Latīnē:

1. Ambulābatne ad lūdum heri Lūcius?
2. Quae (What things) Lūcius vidēre cupiēbat?
3. Quis erat aurīga optimus?
4. Quid clāmābant spectātōrēs?
5. Quid agēbat medicus?

Heri Rūfus medicum bonum visitābat.
Medicus aurīgam īnspectābat.

What was the doctor checking?

| | | |
|---|---|---|
| caput—head | auris—ear | brācchium—arm |
| oculus—eye | collum—neck | manus—hand |
| nāsus—nose | cor—heart | digitus—finger, toe |
| ōs—mouth | stomachus—stomach | crūs—leg |
| lingua—tongue | umbilīcus—navel | pēs—foot |

Label the picture with the Latin names for parts of the body.

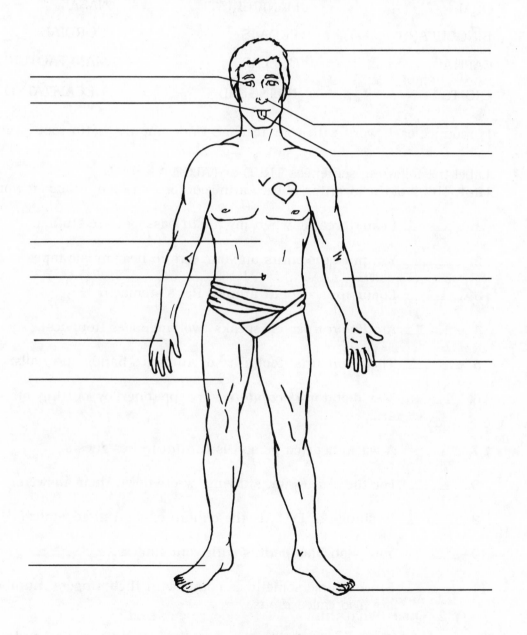

**CORPUS RŪFĪ**

Here are the Latin root-forms from some words for parts of the body:

| caput | "head" | **capit-** | collum | "neck" | **coll-** |
|-------|--------|------------|--------|--------|-----------|
| oculus | "eye" | **ocul-** | cor | "heart" | **cord-** |
| nāsus | "nose" | **nas-** | manus | "hand" | **man-** |
| ōs | "mouth" | **or-** | pēs | "foot" | **ped-** |
| lingua | "tongue" | **lingu-** | digitus | "finger, toe" | **digit-** |

Many English words derive from these Latin root-forms. A few are:

| ORAL | MANICURIST | NASAL |
|------|------------|-------|
| BINOCULARS | PEDALS | CORDIAL |
| CAPITAL | COLLAR | MANUFACTURED |
| DIGITS | BILINGUAL | DECAPITATED |

Pronounce each word with your teacher. Underline the Latin root-forms.

Label the following sentences TRUE or FALSE.
Hint: Think of the meaning of the Latin root-form in each *italicized* word.

1. _____ I can't breathe when my *nasal* passages are stuffed.

2. _____ You put *binoculars* on your ears to hear music tapes.

3. _____ Lucius put a *collar* around Rex's stomach.

4. _____ A *bilingual* person speaks two languages (tongues).

5. _____ The *manicurist* took care of Antonia's hands and nails.

6. _____ The dictator *decapitated* the prisoner by cutting off his arm.

7. _____ A warm-hearted person is *cordial* to her guests.

8. _____ For the *oral* exam, students wrote down their answers.

9. _____ Washington, D.C., is the *capital* of the United States.

10. _____ You push bike *pedals* with your fingers.

11. _____ Since people sometimes count with their fingers, numbers are also called *digits*.

12. _____ The ancient Romans *manufactured* furniture by hand.

Translate:

Ad Circum ambulābat. _____

Ad Circum ambulābant. _____

Remember that **-t** means *he* (or *she* or *it*) and **-nt** means *they*.
Circle the personal endings of the verbs in the Latin sentences.

Here is the complete chart for *walk* in the *past*:

ambulābam *I was walking*        ambulābāmus _____

ambulābās _____        ambulābātis _____

ambulābat _____        ambulābant _____

Translate the forms. Circle the personal endings that come after the **-ba-**.

Here is the complete chart for *to be* in the *past*:

eram *I was*                     erāmus *we were*

erās _____             erātis _____

erat _____             erant _____

Translate the forms. This verb has no **-ba-**. Circle the personal endings.
Remember the *present* forms of *to be*? (Hint: The first one is **sum**, which
means "I am.") It's easy to see the difference between the present and the
past.

## Heri aut Hodiē?

If the verb is *present*, put **Hodiē** (today) in the blank.
If the verb is *past*, put **Heri** (yesterday) in the blank.

1. _____ Pūblius et Lūcius aurīgam spectant.

2. _____ medicus aurīgam spectābat.

3. _____ Claudia erat laeta.

4. _____ clāmābātis in Circō, Lūcī et Pūblī.

5. _____ ānulum cupimus.

6. _____ es pulchra, Amābilis.

7. _____ scrībēbam in tablīnō.

# LECTIŌ XXII

# Nūptiae

## Legāmus!

Although Claudia is only thirteen, she is about to be married. Her father Claudius has made all the arrangements. She has no choice. Luckily, she likes Tiberius, her husband-to-be. He is the oldest son of the senator Aemilius and the brother of her friend Livia. Follow the steps leading to Claudia's wedding by reading the Latin passages below.

### Negōtium "Business Arrangements"

| | |
|---|---|
| In Forō Claudius cum Aemiliō ambulābat. | (1) |
| AEMILIUS: "Fīlius meus fīliam tuam in mātrimōnium dūcere cupit. | (2) |
| Dōtem agāmus!" | (3) |
| CLAUDIUS: "Ita vērō, Aemilī! Tiberius est iuvenis bonus." | (4) |
| Duo patrēs pecūniam consīderābant. Dōtem agēbant. | (5) |

*Vocabulary Help:*

(2) in mātrimōnium dūcere—to lead into marriage, to marry
(3) dōtem agāmus—let's arrange the dowry
(4) iuvenis—young man          (5) pecūniam—money

### Spōnsālia "Engagement Ceremony"

| | |
|---|---|
| Cognātī, affīnēs, et amīcī Claudī spectābant Claudiam et Tiberium. | (1) |
| "Claudiam tibi spondeō, Tiberī," inquit Claudius pater. | (2) |
| "Ānulum aureum in digitō tuō pōnō, Claudia," inquit Tiberius. | (3) |
| "Tē amō, Claudia," susurrābat Tiberius. | (4) |
| Omnēs dōna nūptae offerēbant. Multa bāsia Claudiae dabant. | (5) |

*Vocabulary Help:*

(1) cognātī—family members related by blood
    affīnēs—family members related by marriage, in-laws
(2) Claudiam tibi spondeō—I promise Claudia to you
(3) aureum—golden
    pōnō—I am placing
(4) tē—you
(5) dōna nūptae offerēbant—were offering gifts to the bride
    bāsia Claudiae dabant—they were giving Claudia kisses

## Diēs Nūptiārum "Wedding Day"

On the night before her wedding, Claudia took off her **bulla**, gathered up her toys and dolls, and placed them on the altar of the Lares, the personal gods of the Claudian family. She slept in a new tunic.

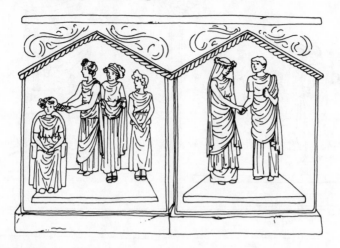

## I. In Cubiculō

| | |
|---|---|
| Sōl lūcēbat. Claudia in cubiculō erat. Nūpta timida erat. | (1) |
| Tunicam rēctam gerēbat. Ānulōs et monīle et armillās gerēbat. | (2) |
| Amābilis capillōs texēbat. Antōnia flammeum tenēbat. | (3) |
| Iūlia, māter Tiberī, rīdēbat. | (4) |
| "Pulcherrima es," inquit, "Tiberius, fīlius meus, fēlīx est." | (5) |

---

### Vocabulary Help:

(2) tunicam rēctam—white, ankle-length wedding gown
   monīle et armillās—necklace and bracelets
(3) capillōs texēbat—was braiding her hair
   flammeum tenēbat—was holding the flame-colored bridal veil
(5) pulcherrima—very beautiful
   fēlīx—lucky

## II. In Ātriō

| | |
|---|---|
| Familia Claudī in ātriō erat. Tiberius cum Līviā et Pūbliō stābat. | (1) |
| Claudia nūpta intrābat. Antōnia et Iūlia lacrimābant. | (2) |
| Iūlia prōnuba, "Dextrās Claudiae et Tiberī iungō," inquit. | (3) |
| Claudia Tiberium spectābat. "Ubi tū Gāius, ego Gāia," inquit. | (4) |
| Spectātōrēs clāmābant, "Fēlīciter! Fēlīciter!" | (5) |
| Omnēs mustāceum edēbant. Vīnum bibēbant. Laetī erant. | (6) |

---

### Vocabulary Help:

(2) lacrimābant—were crying
(3) prōnuba—the bride's attendant
   dextrās. . .iungō—I am joining the right hands
(4) "Ubi tū Gāius, ego Gāia"—"Where you are Gaius, I am Gaia" (bride's vow)
(5) Fēlīciter!—Good luck!
(6) mustāceum—wedding cake

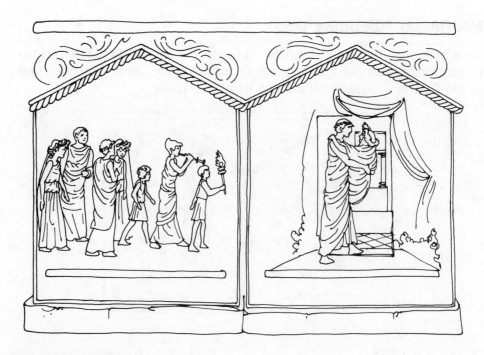

## III. Domus Nova

| | |
|---|---|
| Nocte Claudia, "Dūc mē, Tiberī, domum novam!" inquit. | (1) |
| Domō Claudī exībant. | (2) |
| Cognātī, affīnēs, et amīcī quoque exībant. In viā ambulābant. | (3) |
| Servī taedās portābant. Quattuor tībīcinēs lūdēbant. | (4) |
| Lūcius et Pūblius epithalamium cantābant. | (5) |
| Tandem Tiberius et Claudia domum novam cōnspēxērunt. | (6) |
| Claudia, "Trāns līmen portā mē, Tiberī!" inquit. | (7) |
| Claudia, "Nunc taedam exstinctam ad amīcās iaciō!" inquit. | (8) |
| Līvia, "Eam capiō!" inquit. | (9) |
| "Valēte, Claudia et Tiberī! Fēlīciter!" omnēs clāmābant. | (10) |
| Antōnia et Iūlia lacrimābant. | (11) |

---

*Vocabulary Help:*

(1) nocte—at night
dūc mē!—lead me (to)!
(2) exībant—they were going out of
(3) quoque—also
in viā—on the street
(4) taedās—torches
tībīcinēs—flute players
(5) epithalamium—wedding song
(6) tandem—finally

cōnspēxērunt—caught sight of
(7) trāns līmen—across the threshold
portā mē!—carry me!
(8) taedam exstinctam—a torch that has been extinguished
iaciō—I am throwing
(9) eam capiō—I'm catching it

---

### Then and Now: Wedding Customs

Find at least five ancient Roman wedding customs that are also followed in modern American weddings. If the Roman custom is a little different, describe the difference. For example, Claudia threw an extinguished torch; a modern American bride often throws her bouquet of flowers.

# Language Discovery: Building Blocks II

Here are three Latin sentences with the same types of building blocks:

1. Tiberius ānulum in digitō pōnēbat.
2. Claudius Aemilium in Forō petēbat.
3. Tiberius Claudiam trāns līmen portābat.

Put the building blocks for each sentence in the appropriate list:

| Subjects | Direct Objects | Prepositional Phrases | Verbs |
|---|---|---|---|
| _____ | _____ | _____ | _____ |
| _____ | _____ | _____ | _____ |
| _____ | _____ | _____ | _____ |

Another building block you have seen is called an *adverb*. It usually tells you *how* or *when* the action happened. Compare these sentences:

1. Claudius cum Aemiliō in Forō ambulābat.
2. Heri Claudius cum Aemiliō in Forō ambulābat.

What is the adverb in sentence 2? _____

*When* was Claudius walking with Aemilius? _____

Try building your own Latin sentences with adverbs. Use the building blocks below. Make up five sentences. Be sure they make sense!

| Adverbs | Subjects | Direct Objects | Prepositional Phrases | Verbs |
|---|---|---|---|---|
| māne | nūpta pulchra | pecūniam | in Forō | capit |
| nocte | Lūcius frāter | taedam | in digitō Claudiae | edēbat |
| heri | Tiberius iuvenis | Lūcium | in ātriō magnō | pōnit |
| hodiē | amīca Līvia | mustāceum | in cubiculō parvō | spectat |
| tandem | Amābilis | tunicam rēctam | in viā | gerēbat |
| subitō | Bella fēlēs | capillōs longōs | in culīnā | texēbat |
| mox | pater laetus | Claudiam | trāns līmen | portat |
| iterum | māter trīstis | ānulum aureum | in mēnsā | tenēbat |

Now you can write, read, and speak in Latin. **Congrātulātiōnēs!**

# *Review IV*

## Verba Latīna

Match the Latin noun with its meaning.

1. thermae        _____ ring

2. medicus       _____ wedding dress

3. collum         _____ young man

4. ānulus         _____ doctor

5. via              _____ horse

6. tunica rēcta    _____ road, street

7. iuvenis        _____ school

8. equus          _____ neck

9. barba          _____ beard

10. lūdus         _____ baths

Match the Latin verb with its meaning.

1. portat         _____ she joins

2. texit          _____ she throws

3. iungit         _____ she braids

4. legit          _____ she holds

5. tenet         _____ she carries

6. iacit          _____ she writes

7. gerit         _____ she hears, listens

8. scrībit       _____ she wears

9. dūcit        _____ she reads

10. audit        _____ she leads

# Word Search: Corpus

Find and circle the Latin words for the parts of the body pictured. Words may go across, down, or on the diagonal, but they are never backward.

```
U R S A N A S U S
O M T U C A P U T
D O B R M R E B M
I C E I A T U P A
G U N S L U O S N
I L P E S I X A U
T U A C O R C E S
U S Q L I N G U A
S T O M A C H U S
```

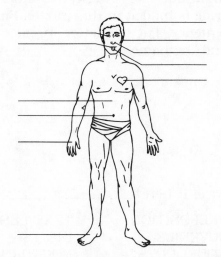

## Pair Them Up!

The verbs below are all mixed up. Find the eight verbs that are *present* and list them in the **present** column. Then pair each verb with its *past* form. Be sure the personal endings agree. The first two are done for you.

| | | | |
|---|---|---|---|
| sum | audiēbat | capis | erat |
| audit | audītis | sunt | capiēbāmus |
| erant | capiēbās | capimus | est |
| audiēbātis | eram | audiō | audiēbam |

| Present | Past |
|---|---|
| *sum* | *eram* |
| *audit* | *audiēbat* |
| _____ | _____ |
| _____ | _____ |
| _____ | _____ |
| _____ | _____ |
| _____ | _____ |
| _____ | _____ |

**61**

# Word Game

## A Bride for Lucius

When Lucius is twenty years old, he will marry. The name of his future bride is hidden in this puzzle. Find the English word that completes each sentence. Put one letter in each blank. Read down the circled letters to find the name.

Write it here: _____  _____

PREPOSITION    TEXTILES    CAPTURE    EJECT
JUVENILE    DIGITS    NASAL    TENANT
AQUEDUCTS    NOCTURNAL    THERMOS    JUNCTION

1. A young person is not an adult; he's a _ _ Ⓞ _ _ _ _ _.

2. You breathe through your two _ Ⓞ _ _ _ passages.

3. Cotton and wool are woven materials or _ _ _ _ _ Ⓞ _ _.

4. The teacher tried to throw out or Ⓞ _ _ _ _ the bad student.

5. Owls and bats stay awake at night; they're called

   _ _ _ _ _ Ⓞ _ _ _ animals.

6. The numbers 0, 1, 2, 3, 4, 5, 6, 7, 8, and 9 are _ Ⓞ _ _ _ _.

7. To lead water over uneven stretches of land, Romans built

   bridge-like structures called Ⓞ _ _ _ _ _ _ _ _.

8. A word that is placed in front of a noun to make a phrase is called

   a Ⓞ _ _ _ _ _ _ _ _ _ _.

9. The police were not able to _ _ _ _ _ Ⓞ _ the escaped

   convict.

10. The place where two roads join is called a _ _ _ _ _ Ⓞ _ _.

11. To keep liquids hot in winter, use a _ _ _ _ Ⓞ _ _.

12. A person who rents an apartment is the _ _ _ Ⓞ _ _.

Each statement below is false. To make it true, cross out one word or phrase that is incorrect and write a correct word above it. For example,

The training of young Roman girls was their *mothers'* ~~fathers'~~ responsibility.

1. Romans at the Baths cleansed themselves with soap.

2. The public Baths contained gardens, restaurants, and hotel rooms in addition to the bathing rooms.

3. The husband of a girl in ancient Rome was chosen by her mother.

4. The average age of a girl getting married for the first time was eighteen.

5. The Roman bride's wedding veil was made of white silk.

6. The wedding ceremony was held in the garden of the bride's house.

7. The Roman Forum contained government buildings, temples to the gods, and apartment houses.

8. A man who cut men's hair and trimmed their beards was a **scriba**.

9. A man who took care of sick people in ancient Rome was a **pictor**.

10. The largest racetrack in ancient Rome was the Colosseum.

11. Roman children went to school about 9:00 a.m.

12. Roman elementary schoolchildren wrote their answers on paper.

13. Besides Latin, Roman schoolchildren studied the English language.

14. To figure out arithmetic problems, Roman schoolchildren used a calculator.

# Valēte!

Here are some members of Claudius' **familia**. Write *three* sentences that describe each family member. Use the verbs supplied for you.

_Lūcius_ est _puer_____.
_Lūcius ad lūdum_____ ambulat.
_Lūcius fābulam_____ legit.

_____ est _____.
_____ lūdit.
_____ amat.

_____ est _____.
_____ gerit.
_____ sedet.

_____ est _____.
_____ gerit.
_____ edit.

_____ est _____.
_____ coquit.
_____ spectat.

_____ est _____.
_____ bibit.
_____ audit.

_____ est _____.
_____ habitat.
_____ vēndit.

64